PLATE I.

JOHN CUNNINGHAM SAUNDERS.
From an engraving by Anthony Cardon, after a picture by A. W. Devis.

Frontispiece

THE HISTORY & TRADITIONS
OF THE
MOORFIELDS EYE HOSPITAL

ONE HUNDRED YEARS OF
OPHTHALMIC DISCOVERY & DEVELOPMENT

BY

E. TREACHER COLLINS

CONSULTING SURGEON; MEMBER OF THE COMMITTEE OF MANAGEMENT;
FORMERLY, CLINICAL ASSISTANT; JUNIOR AND SENIOR HOUSE
SURGEON; CURATOR OF THE MUSEUM AND LIBRARIAN;
ASSISTANT SURGEON AND SURGEON

WITH TWENTY-SEVEN PLATES

LONDON
H. K. LEWIS & CO. LTD.
1929

Published in 1929 by H. K. Lewis & Co. Ltd.
Reprinted Lithographically in 1974
by Headley Brothers Ltd., The Invicta Press,
Ashford, Kent.

DEDICATED TO THE MEMORY

OF THE

MEMBERS OF THE SURGICAL STAFF

OF THE

MOORFIELDS EYE HOSPITAL

IN THE YEARS 1883 TO 1887

TO WHOSE INFLUENCE AND INSTRUCTION
THE AUTHOR IS SO DEEPLY INDEBTED

PREFACE

GREAT traditions are the most valuable assets which a hospital or a teaching establishment can possess. They give it a personality which makes it beloved and respected. Traditions are made up of the energies and enterprise of those who have gone before, and will live on from generation to generation long after the bones of those who have created them have crumbled into dust. The primary aim of this book is to put on record the traditions of the Moorfields Eye Hospital for the benefit of past, present, and future workers within its walls.

So intimately associated has this Hospital been with all the discoveries and developments which have taken place in connection with ophthalmology during the nineteenth century, that it was not possible to write a history of the first hundred years of its existence without giving an account of them also. By having done this, it is hoped that the book may find a wider circle of readers than those for whom it was in the first instance intended.

An endeavour has been made to give an account of events as they have happened in chronological order, and by so doing to produce the effect of a cinematograph film, rather than that of an album of photographs.

For the facts recorded, numerous different sources have been tapped. Much information as to the commencement of the Institution has been derived from Barnsby Cooper's biography of his uncle, Sir Astley Cooper. Great use has been made of the minute books of the Committee of Management of the Hospital, and of its annual reports.

For biographical details, the *Dictionary of National Biography* has been consulted, and also the articles on the

" British Masters of Ophthalmology " which have been published in the *British Journal of Ophthalmology*.

It has been said that " when a medical man begins to write on the history of his subject it is a sure sign of senility." The writer of these traditions does not claim that his case is any exception to this rule. In early life a man has to learn history. In middle life he is engaged in making history; and it is in his later years that he becomes best qualified to write history. It is then that, on looking back, he obtains the most comprehensive view, and is able to regard objects in their truest perspective.

In conclusion I have to thank the Committee of Management of the Hospital for its permission to reproduce the portraits of several former members of the surgical staff, which hang in its Board Room; also the *British Journal of Ophthalmology* for permission to use the blocks of some of the illustrations which have been published in its pages; and lastly my friend Mr. Frank Juler for kindly reading through and correcting the proof-sheets.

CONTENTS

LIST OF PLATES

xi

THE HISTORY AND TRADITIONS OF THE MOORFIELDS EYE HOSPITAL

CHAPTER I

THE FOUNDERS AND FOUNDATION

In the board room of the Royal London Ophthalmic Hospital hangs a framed document in which the names of Saunders, Farre, and Battley are associated as being the first promoters of the institution.

Who were these three men ? What brought them together ? And how came they to establish an institution unlike any which had previously existed ?

John Cunningham Saunders was born and bred in Devonshire; he first saw the light of day at Levistone on October 10th, 1773. He went to school at Tavistock and South Molton, and at the age of seventeen commenced a five years' apprenticeship to Mr. John Hill, surgeon, of Barnstaple. It was during his apprenticeship that he had his first introduction to ophthalmic surgery, for Mr. Hill, though only a country practitioner, was bold enough in those pre-anæsthetic days to operate for cataract. It was from him also that Saunders first learnt the value of the use of belladonna for dilatation of the pupil. William Adams, who also became an ophthalmic surgeon, was likewise a pupil of Mr. John Hill, but of him more anon.

Saunders, at the expiration of his apprenticeship, came to London to complete his medical education at the then combined borough schools of St. Thomas's and Guy's Hospitals. The skill and diligence which he displayed in the dissecting room, together with his deftness as a draftsman, soon attracted the attention of Astley Cooper, who was then rapidly rising into fame. On Cooper's election to the chair of anatomy in 1797, he offered to take Saunders into his house and make him a demonstrator of anatomy on the terms shown in the following letter:

" DEAR SIR,
    " I ought long since to have informed you of my plan for the winter, so far as it concerns you, and as I have been able to decide.
    " It is my wish that you should lodge and board in my house. I have informed you that I live in a plain and economical style, and that you are only to expect a joint of meat and a pudding; if this will satisfy you, a bed will be ready whenever you return to London.
    " I can say nothing about the salary you are to receive, for I have not been able to form any idea of what will be proper, or how much you may expect; all I can say is that the sum shall be annually increased, which at the same time as it may act as a stimulus to you, and make it an object to proceed in your career, will be more convenient to myself, because, if no stroke of adverse fortune prevents it, my income must be yearly improving.
    " It is my wish that you should dissect for lecture-work in Comparative Anatomy, and assist in my preparations. With respect to the first of these, the labour is certain, and all other occupations and objects must yield to it; with regard to the latter, the quantum of employment shall be guided by your feelings. It is a duty I have performed, without injury to my health, with much amusement, and great advantage.
    " I am in hopes that you will have no objection to giving me three months' information if any other pursuit should lead you to quit the situation, as otherwise, I may be unable to procure a substitute, and suffer great inconvenience from the want of one."

Saunders accepted the offer, and was shortly afterwards appointed the demonstrator of anatomy at St. Thomas's Hospital. His association with Astley Cooper proved an exceedingly happy one, he on several occasions being entrusted with the charge of Cooper's patients during his absence in the country. Saunders was evidently a good teacher, and possessed of a most attractive personality, so that he became exceedingly popular with the students, who on several occasions presented him with pieces of plate as a token of their regard.

John Richard Farre was two years younger than Saunders, being born in Barbados in 1775, where he was educated, and commenced the study of medicine under his father. He came to England in 1792 to complete his studies at St. Thomas's and Guy's Hospitals. The commencement of his acquaintance with Saunders and Battley may best be given in his own words:

" In 1792 I entered as a dresser at Guy's Hospital. At that time Sir Astley Cooper had, by his open manner, become well known among the pupils, but I was not intimate with him, until after my return, in 1794, from the expedition in which I served under Lord Moria. I then became more particularly acquainted with him in the following manner.

" About the year 1798, Sir Astley excited great zeal in the prosecution of minute anatomy, and the order of the day became the injection of the absorbents, and the dissection of parts concerned in operations, especially those of hernia. It was at this time that my acquaintance commenced with Mr. Saunders and Mr. Battley, who were both engaged in the dissecting room. So earnest were we all in the pursuit of the subjects above described, that Mr. Saunders and myself became jaundiced, in consequence of the continually constrained position to which we were subjected, while leaning over bodies under dissection.

" Mr. Saunders also suffered from a punctured wound of the finger received while dissecting, which was followed by extensive inflammation of the arm; nor did this subside until nearly two hundred leeches had been applied."

Richard Battley was older than his two friends, having been born at Wakefield in 1770; he was educated at the Grammar School there, and subsequently became the pupil of a physician in that town. For a while he studied at the Infirmary in Newcastle-on-Tyne, and came to London in 1795. Entering as a pupil at St. Thomas's Hospital at the same time as Saunders, a close and lasting intimacy sprang up between the two men.

Having thus brought these three men together from Devonshire, Bermuda, and Wakefield to the dissecting room at St. Thomas's Hospital, it next becomes necessary to trace the circumstances which led them to start the " London Dispensary for Curing Diseases of the Eye and Ear," the name by which the present " Royal London Ophthalmic Hospital " was first known.

In 1800, when twenty-seven years of age, Saunders became anxious about his future prospects.   His ambition prompted him with the desire to practise as a surgeon in London; probably also about this time influences began to work which made him desire to settle down with an assured income, so that he might enter into the state of matrimony.   There was little prospect of his obtaining any higher appointment than that of demonstrator of anatomy in the hospital at which he was working, the custom in the old-established hospitals at that time being to select for the staff appointments a pupil of one of their surgeons, and one who had been articled at the Royal College of Surgeons for at least six years.   Saunders had not been so articled, having served his apprenticeship in the country.   He was not, therefore, eligible to compete against those who had proceeded in the recognised manner, no matter how great his merits.   This was pointed out to him by Astley Cooper, who advised him in his own interests to seek some other means of support. Saunders then resigned his post as demonstrator of anatomy and took over the practice of a surgeon in Gravesend.

Astley Cooper, however, soon began to miss his able assistant, and found that the other arrangements he had made, which had to some extent caused Saunders to take offence, did not work smoothly.   He therefore wrote him the following letter, and induced Saunders' friend Battley to go to Gravesend to use his influence in persuading him to resume his old post:

" London,
" *July 28th*, 1801.

" Dear Sir,
" I have so often explained my reasons for the change
which I made last winter at the Hospital, that I consider it
as almost unnecessary to say anything further upon the
subject. The trial has been made; Mr. D—— has been
weighed against you in the balance, and been found want-
ing.

" His excessive vanity has disgusted, his want of perseverance has disappointed, me, and I feel most thoroughly
convinced that his abilities are inadequate to the task which
has been assigned to him.

" I felt it my duty to act as I have done, and my conduct,
I fear, has been the cause of uneasiness to you; but as our
separation was not the effect of misconduct upon your part,
or of any disapprobation on mine, I hope we shall be again
united in the pursuit of medical science, and that we shall
entertain for each other that respect and esteem which I must
ever feel for you.

" As I told you in our last conversation, I have ever felt
a degree of veneration for your acquirements and abilities,
which has made me diffident in expressing my wishes. But
as you have now courted it, I will say, that I have wished to
see you join in the debates of Guy's Medical Society. The
capability of expressing our ideas in public is a source of
more power than anything with which I am acquainted.
It is the road to bring a public teacher to character and to
fortune.

" *Secondly*, I should much wish for your assistance in
making experiments upon animals. I am certain that
everything valuable in physiology is only to be so obtained.
What is every day under observation of the senses is well
known, but few men have sufficient knowledge of anatomy
to be capable of making the interior parts of the body the
subject of inquiry.

" *Thirdly*, you will do me a favour by making my collection
in comparative anatomy more complete. This, I am aware,
is the greatest favour I can ask, as you are neither captivated
by its splendour nor convinced of its utility; but as I have
embarked on it, you will confer an obligation upon me by
assisting me in making it complete.

" I shall endeavour to make your situation comfortable

in a pecuniary point of view, but I had rather make that the subject of conversation when I see you.

"I am, dear Sir,

"Yours, with the utmost esteem,

"A. C."

Battley had a high appreciation of his friend's talents, and felt strongly that they would not have sufficient scope in such a confined sphere as Gravesend. The combined effect of his persuasive influence, and of Cooper's letter, ultimately induced Saunders to resume the duties of demonstrator of anatomy at St. Thomas's.

Shortly afterwards he took a house in Ely Place, with the intention of practising as a surgeon, and on April 7th, 1803, married Miss Jane Louisa Colkett.

During the last years of the eighteenth and the first years of the nineteenth centuries England was at war with France. Farre, in 1793, went with Lord Moira's expedition to France, returning, however, to London on its failure. Battley for a time served in the Navy as an assistant surgeon, and was present at several engagements under Sir Sidney Smith.

In 1799 Napoleon invaded Egypt, and after the destruction of his fleet by Nelson at the Battle of the Nile, English troops under Sir Ralph Abercrombie were landed at Aboukir, in 1800. Almost all were attacked by what was called "Egyptian ophthalmia," but which we now know must have been a mixed infection of purulent ophthalmia and trachoma. After the evacuation of Egypt by the English in 1803, the troops were disbanded, and spread this very infectious form of eye disease in all the stations at which they stopped and throughout Great Britain.

Mr. Patrick Macgregor, surgeon to the Royal Military Asylum, writes of the effects of the disease in the Army as follows:

"The progress of the ophthalmia since its first introduction into this country in the year 1800 has, in the Army, been very rapid and extensive, and has at different periods materially interfered with its discipline and efficiency. It has crippled many of our best regular regiments to such a degree as for a time to render them unfit for service; and though the regiments which were in Egypt have, in general, suffered most from the disease, yet it has prevailed extensively in others which have never served in that country."

The terribly destructive character of the disease may be shown by its effects on the second battalion of the 52nd Light Infantry, which are recorded by Dr. Vetch: out of 636 cases 50 were dismissed with the loss of both eyes, and 40 with that of one.

The spread of the disease was not confined to the Army, but extended widely throughout the country in the towns and villages, when the disbanded troops returned to their homes carrying infection with them.

That the medical men and the hospitals in this country were badly prepared to deal with such an immense increase in eye diseases may be shown by quoting a description of the condition of things which then existed, written by Sir William Lawrence some thirty years later:

" The diseases of the eye, in general hospitals, are inadequate, from the smallness of their number, to the purposes of practical study, particularly that of exemplifying the various operations. Thus these institutions have been inefficient in reference to this important department. As the general body of surgeons did not understand diseases of the eye, the public naturally resorted to ' oculists ' " [in speaking of " oculists " he refers to those that have bestowed that title on themselves without having had any regular medical training] " who, seeing such cases in greater numbers, became better acquainted with the symptoms, diagnosis, and treatment; and especially more skilful in the operative department. At the same time, the subject, being imperfectly understood, was neglected in the general surgical courses, in which many important affections were entirely unnoticed, and the whole very inadequately explained. Thus students, who resorted to London for the completion of their professional studies, had no means of learning this important department of the profession, which was tacitly abandoned, even by the hospital surgeons, and turned over to the 'oculists.' The latter, not being conversant with the principles derived from anatomy, physiology, and general pathology, attended merely to the organ, and relied almost exclusively on what is comparatively of little importance, local treatment. Hence ophthalmic surgery, being in a manner dismembered from the general science, was reduced to a very low ebb. Until within a few years, it was, in this country at least, in a state of almost total darkness."

It will thus be seen that at the time Saunders established himself as a surgeon in London there was an immense increase in the amount of eye disease, but that very few medical men were in any way trained or competent to deal with it, and scanty, if any, provision was made for its treatment in the hospitals.

Saunders' attention had early in his career been attracted to diseases of the eye during his apprenticeship under Mr. John Hill, and his studies in the dissecting room had afforded him a sound basis for their treatment, in an intimate knowledge of the anatomy of the organ and its surrounding structures. His association with Astley Cooper had also led him to devote special attention to the anatomy of the ear and to disorders of hearing. Astley Cooper in 1800 made a communication to the Royal Society, on the effects of destruction of the tympanic membrane of the ear. He had found that considerable openings might be made in it without impairment of the hearing power, and was thereby led to perform the operation of puncturing the membrane in cases of deafness resulting from obstruction in the Eustachian tube, with a remarkably good result in the restoration of hearing, in the first cases in which he employed it. Subsequent experience, however, showed it not to be so generally useful as he had originally anticipated. He made a second communication on the same subject in the following year, and in 1802 was elected a Fellow of the Royal Society, and awarded the Copley Medal.

Whilst these papers were being written the subject of them must have been much discussed by Cooper and his assistant Saunders, the latter's interest in ear disease being thereby awakened.

On starting in practice at Ely Place, Saunders decided to devote himself to the treatment of diseases of the eye and ear, a decision which must have required considerable courage at that time by one who wished to remain of good repute with other members of his profession. Up to that time the treatment of eye diseases had been mainly in the hands of itinerant quacks, who dubbed themselves oculists.

George Coats, who has written an account of the lives and practices of many of these worthies, has well described the condition of things which then existed. He says:

" In the eighteenth century ophthalmology had not yet vindicated, in England, its position as a separate branch of practice. It was the province of a set of ambulant practitioners who toured the country accompanied by all the apparatus of shameless advertisement (including 'monkies,' we are told), couching cataracts, and selling infallible salves and eyewashes. This taint of quackery appears to have deterred respectable surgeons from meddling much with the subject; their operative experience was probably small, and the procedure of couching, attended frequently with brilliant immediate, but disastrous after, results, was likely to be performed with fewer scruples by itinerant oculists, here to-day and gone to-morrow, than by settled practitioners who had to abide the consequences of their handiwork."

Such men were naturally looked upon as charlatans by the medical profession, but that did not prevent them becoming the recipients of royal favours.

One William Read, who commenced life as a tailor, and became a mountebank and itinerant quack oculist, settled in London in 1694, advertising in the *Tatler* " that he had been thirty-five years in the practice of couching cataracts, taking off all sorts of wens, curing wry necks and hair-lips [*sic*] without blemish." In 1705 he was knighted, " as a mark of royal favour for his great services, done in curing great numbers of seamen and soldiers of blindness gratis "; and about the same time was appointed oculist-in-ordinary to Queen Anne. It is stated that the wealth he acquired enabled him to mix with the best literary society of the day. Swift, in writing to Stella, commented on the quality of his punch which he served in golden vessels. One sample of his methods of treatment need only be quoted—" the putting of a louse into the eye when it is dull and obscure, and wanteth humours and spirits. This," he says, " tickleth and pricketh, so that it maketh the eye moist and rheumatick and quickeneth the spirits."

On Sir William Read's death in 1715, his rival, Roger Grant, succeeded to the post of oculist to Queen Anne, and afterwards to George I. Grant, originally a cobbler and later a Baptist minister, lost one eye as a soldier in the service of the German Emperor, and then set up as an oculist in Mouse Alley, Wapping. He advertised profusely in the journals of the day, giving accounts of his cures, with certificates attached from the patients themselves and others.

George II. appointed as his oculist-in-ordinary John Taylor, better known as " Chevalier Taylor," of whom Coats says:

" Amongst travelling quacks the name of the ' Chevalier ' Taylor stands pre-eminent for unblushing effrontery, blatant self-laudation, and all the methods of the charlatan, but also for mental endowments far above the average of his tribe, and for real acquaintance with the contemporary state of ophthalmic knowledge. His fame extended to every country in Europe; his boast of having conversed with kings and princes is no idle one; he had an acquaintance, not always felicitous, with some of the best known men, medical and lay, of his time; counting translations and minor works he was the author of nearly fifty books; and in later life he wrote an autobiography, which, if it gives few and unreliable particulars as to his actions, does much to reveal the character of the man."

The Chevalier's talents seem to have been hereditary, for his son and two grandsons followed the same line of practice, and were each in turn the recipients of royal favours.

It was with such prating mountebanks that Saunders ran the risk of being confused in devoting himself specially to the treatment of eye diseases. He was not, however, the first reputable medical practitioner in London to specialise in this line of work, having been preceded by both Wathen and James Ware. Dr. Wathen published, in 1785, *A Dissertation on the Theory and Cure of Cataract*, and held the appointment of oculist to George III. He took Ware when a young man into partnership with him, a partnership which lasted for fourteen years, during which time Ware acquired such a liking for eye work that he decided to devote himself exclusively to it.

Ware, like Saunders, had studied at St. Thomas's Hospital, and held there the post of demonstrator of anatomy, so it would seem highly probable that his example may have had some influence in determining Saunders to take up surgery of the eye as a special branch of practice.

In 1801 Ware contributed to the Royal Society a paper dealing with the case of a boy of seven years of age upon whom he had operated for cataract, and as the result of this communication he was elected a Fellow of the Royal Society. It was one of Saunders' most noteworthy achievements, as we shall see later, to introduce an operation for cataract in infants who are born blind.

The suggestion that Saunders should start a special institution for the treatment of diseases of the eye and ear is stated by Battley to have originated with Astley Cooper, whose own experience, in the treatment of diseases of the ear, had shown him what insufficient accommodation the General Hospitals offered for the treatment of diseases of the special organs. As his letters show, he held a very high opinion of Saunders' professional abilities, and he saw only too clearly that the nature of Saunders' apprenticeship would prevent him being promoted to any surgical post at either of the Borough Hospitals. Consequently the idea suggested itself to him that a special hospital might be established for diseases of the eye and ear, at which Saunders might find a suitable field for the exercise of his skill and ingenuity.

Before taking any action in the matter, Saunders first sought the advice of the physicians and surgeons of St. Thomas's and Guy's Hospitals, and having obtained from them a testimonial of their approbation, on October 1st, 1804, he published the following proposal for instituting " A Dispensary for the Poor afflicted with Diseases of the Eye and Ear," with their testimonial attached:

" Among the many charitable institutions which mark the wisdom and benevolence of the inhabitants of this Metropolis there is none particularly appropriated to the relief of the poor afflicted with diseases of the Eye and Ear. No diseases which do not affect the life of the patient are more distressing than such as are incident to these organs or demand greater dexterity and skill in their treatment. The structure of the Eye and Ear is so delicate and complex and their irritability under injury so extreme, that they cannot easily be treated but by those who make them the objects of peculiar study and attention. The acknowledged difficulty in the treatment of the diseases to which they are liable has induced a few to separate themselves from the general practice of professional duties and to devote themselves to the exercise of this branch alone, a fact which sufficiently establishes the necessity of making them the objects of a specific institution. Every surgeon must allow that most unremitting care and attention is necessary after some of the capital operations on the eye, and that through the want of it some of the most dexterous operations are frequently defeated. In large hospitals and dispensaries which embrace a variety of objects, where the medical attendants are deeply interested in the most formidable and excruciating diseases, it can rarely happen that sufficient leisure is afforded for the exercise of that strict care and attention which operations on the eye demand, much less will it happen, when patients are the subjects of fortuitous operations and retire afterwards to their own homes where they experience a miserable want of every comfort and convenience, that such operation can be successful. Impressed with these considerations the author of this address, who devotes himself to the treatments of diseases of the Eye and the Ear, solicits the public to patronise an institution which will enable him to extend relief to the poor afflicted with these diseases. An institution of this kind will be the means of restoring to society the exertions of many industrious individuals and will be established and carried on at a very moderate expense. The author of this address offers his services to the Charity without any emolument to himself and he pledges himself to the promoters of the institution, that the public shall reap the fruits of their beneficence.

" J. C. SAUNDERS,

" *Surgeon and Demonstrator of Practical Anatomy at St. Thomas's Hospital.*

" 24, ELY PLACE, HOLBORN,
" *October 1st, 1804.*"

" We are of the opinion that the establishment of the dispensary will prove beneficial, and is therefore worthy of public support, and that the author of the proposal is qualified to procure the accomplishment of its object.

Signed:

Physicians of St. Thomas's.	*Physicians of Guy's.*
Wm. Lister, M.D.	Wm. Babington, M.D.
W. C. Wills, M.D.	James Curry, M.D.
Thos. Turner, M.D.	M. Alexander, M.D.
G. Gilbert Currey, M.D.	
Surgeons of St. Thomas's.	*Surgeons of Guy's.*
G. Chander.	T. Foster.
I. Birch.	Wm. Lucas.
H. Cline.	Astley Cooper."

As the outcome of the issue of this circular a committee was formed which held its first meeting at the City Coffee House on January 4th, 1805, Mr. Benjamin Travers, a wealthy City merchant and the father of the surgeon of the same name, being in the chair.

This Mr. Benjamin Travers, Sen., in the keen pursuit of knowledge, had attended Astley Cooper's lectures on anatomy, and had become so interested in them and the lecturer, that he apprenticed his son to him as a pupil, and later extended his patronage to the project of founding an eye dispensary put forward by Cooper's demonstrator and protégé.

At the meeting the following resolutions were moved and unanimously agreed to:

"That a dispensary be instituted under the name of the London Dispensary for the Relief of the Poor afflicted with Diseases of the Eye and the Ear, where they may apply and obtain advice and medicines gratis.

"That the dispensary be situated in a central part of this city and contain beds for the reception of patients who undergo the operation for the cataract or any other operation of the eye requiring minute care.

"That the Charity consist of a Treasurer, Governors, Secretary, and Medical Officers.

"That Henry Kensington, Esq., be appointed Treasurer.

"That a person contributing an annual subscription of one guinea be a governor and have the right of recommending and keeping under the care of the charity one out-patient, and if two guineas, two out-patients, and so in proportion to his subscription.

"That patients admitted into the house be admitted according to priority of recommendation, except in cases of emergency, when the medical officers must determine.

"That Mr. J. C. Saunders be appointed Surgeon of the Dispensary, and that Dr. Farre be appointed Consulting Physician in cases requiring medical aid."

Richard Battley, who was then practising as an apothecary in St. Paul's Churchyard, undertook the duties of Secretary, which he continued to discharge in an honorary capacity, with the utmost assiduity, for fourteen years.

Many City merchants, with whom Saunders had no previous acquaintance, became subscribers, and sufficient funds were soon forthcoming to provide for the purchase of the lease of No. 40, Charterhouse Square, for eighteen years, for the sum of £300 and an annual rental of £65.

SHOWING THE SOUTH SIDE OF CHARTERHOUSE SQUARE AND NO. 40.

Where the London Dispensary for Curing Diseases of the Eye and Ear was first opened in 1805.

[To face p. 14

On March 25th, 1805, *The London Dispensary for Curing Diseases of the Eye and Ear* was opened for the reception of patients.

Sir Charles Price, Bart., a former Lord Mayor, and Member of Parliament for the City of London, accepted the post of President of the Institution, and several of the Aldermen of the City became its Vice-Presidents.

One Sarah Clark was appointed nurse and housekeeper, she being required to act under the control of the Surgeon, who had power to dismiss her for misconduct. She was allowed coals and candles and a gratuity at the end of the year " such as the Committee may deem proportionate to her services." Her husband was subsequently engaged to dispense drugs, and the two of them received £50 a year for their services, together with the aforesaid coals and candles.

In 1804, after Saunders had brought forward his proposal for the establishment of an Eye Dispensary, Mr. Wathen (afterwards Sir Wathen Waller), an oculist of eminence, described to King George III. the sad state of the soldiers and sailors who had returned from the campaign in Egypt suffering from ophthalmia, and suggested the desirability of establishing an Infirmary exclusively for eye diseases: " Their Majesties and the Royal Family graciously and humanely approved of the plan, and honoured it with their patronage and benefactions." Such was the origin of the Royal Infirmary for Diseases of the Eye, in Cork Street, which commenced under Mr. Wathen, and was subsequently carried on as a comparatively private institution, under the charge of Mr. Charles Alexander, up to the time of his death in 1872.

This institution must not be confused with that started in the Western district of London, by the Army surgeon Guthrie, in 1816, which exists to-day as the Royal Westminster Ophthalmic Hospital.

That Wathen's Infirmary was opened for the reception of patients three months before the London Dispensary, though the proposal for its establishment was not made until after the publication of Saunders' circular, evidently caused the latter considerable annoyance, for in a letter addressed to the Committee of the Dispensary in 1808 Saunders writes:

" Subsequently to the date of my Proposal, a similar Institution, honoured with the Royal Patronage, was formed and established in Westminster. Although the Prospectus of the Royal Infirmary was not heard of until many months after the Publication of my Proposal, yet it must be admitted that that Institution first appeared before the Public in a regular and organised form, and this, which is the original, is consequently considered by all who are unacquainted with the facts as the copy. Apprehensive of this impression, I immediately claimed by public advertisements, which were never answered, the priority of my Proposal.

" I should be excused for thus obtruding on your notice if I sought merely the indulgence of honest pride, by maintaining this just claim to respect, but I shall yet more readily be excused, when you reflect, that if I had abandoned this claim, the Public would continue to regard me as an humble copyist."

This Royal Infirmary, whose rivalry at its commencement caused Saunders so much annoyance, continued in existence until Alexander's death in 1872. It was then resolved at a meeting of its Life Governors and Subscribers to close the Institution and to hand over the balance of its funds, after the settlement of all its liabilities, to the Royal London Ophthalmic Hospital. Two hundred pounds was ultimately received by the Hospital, and three of the Committee of the old Infirmary were elected as Life Governors, one of them being a relative of the late Mr. Alexander.

CHAPTER II

THE WORK OF JOHN CUNNINGHAM SAUNDERS

THAT the Institution which Saunders had founded provided a much felt want is evident from the following statement of the number of patients with eye diseases dealt with, and the numbers stated to be " cured," during the first four years of its existence.

1st year, 1805, admitted 600, cured 500.
2nd year, 1806, admitted 1,526, cured 1,036.
3rd year, 1807, admitted 2,126, cured 1,796.
4th year, 1808, admitted 2,357, cured 1,970.

It must be admitted that it is somewhat doubtful what the term " cured " actually implied, for in a list of the diseases which those " cured " suffered from are included some, such as total opacity of the cornea, for which even to-day no absolute cure is known.

Successful as the Institution proved to be in dealing with eye disease, it was far less so in connection with ear disease.

Saunders' first publication was a book entitled *The Anatomy of the Ear: A Treatise on the Diseases of that Organ. The Causes of Deafness and their Treatment.* It must evidently have met with much demand, for a third edition was published after his death, in 1829. Although he had devoted so much study to the treatment of diseases of this organ, he seems soon to have realised that the interests of his Institution would be best served by restricting its aims to the treatment of diseases of the eye only. His reasons for doing so are set out in the following letter which he sent to the Committee in December, 1807:

" Gentlemen,

" Antecedent to the establishment of this Dispensary the diseases of the Eye and Ear had never been made the object of a specific institution, although their great variety and complexity seem to require the most minute and attentive investigation. Those who have practised on the eye have always partially cultivated the ear, and when I chose the former for professed pursuit, the latter also became the subject of my serious enquiry. I had ascertained by observation that certain cases of disease are alleviable. Still I was aware how little would be the success, as the most complicated structure of the organ, which occupies an inaccessible part of our frame, is most frequently the seat of disease. Regardless of this conviction and solely influenced by a knowledge of the positive good which the deaf occasionally receive, I did combine in my proposal for the institution of this charity, the ear with the eye, solicitous of gaining public esteem by doing for the public all the good in my power. But the experience which this institution affords demonstrated the proportion of curable and incurable cases, a proportion much smaller than was expected, at most exceeding (obstruction from inspissated wax excepted) one in a hundred. It grieves me now to state, this branch of our institution exhausts the funds without an adequate advantage, and consumes a portion of my time on an impracticable point, that must ultimately tend to diminish my reputation. The performance of this part of my duty is, therefore, irksome to me, not because it is laborious, but because it neither leads to distinction nor obtains even the common reward of benevolent institutions. To be thankful for intended benefits demands a refinement of reason which none but liberal minds possess. Of those who are dismissed incurable more are made vindictive by disappointment than are grateful for the care bestowed upon them, and the former almost universally represent him who has ineffectually attempted their relief as the author of their misfortunes.

" My attention to the vast number of irremediably deaf which are accumulated at the Charity is not merely disagreeable to my feelings, but absolutely injurious to my interest by causing me to be considered as an Aurist when I am in fact an Oculist. The branch of the profession has always been in my private practice a secondary object. In this light I should wish it to be placed in the Dispensary.

The Ear may consistently with the preservation of those privileges which the Governors have acquired be withdrawn from public notice. Then, whilst I render the same service to those for whom they may individually be interested, it will cease to operate to my prejudice. The mode to be adopted for the accomplishment of this object is implicitly submitted to your judgment.

" I am, gentlemen,

" Your obedient servant,

" J. C. SAUNDERS."

After consideration of this letter by the Governors it was resolved, at a General Meeting in the following January:

" That diseases of the Eye shall in future be the sole object of the Charity, and that its name be changed to that of The London Infirmary for Curing Diseases of the Eye."

In June, 1806, Saunders published an Essay " On Inflammation of the Iris, and the Influence of the Extract of Belladonna to prevent the Consequent Obliteration of the Pupil." In it he gives an accurate description of the clinical characteristics of the affection, and records several cases treated at the Dispensary in which he had prevented loss of sight from closure of the pupils by keeping them dilated with the extract of belladonna, applied to the conjunctiva whilst the inflammation lasted.

In January, 1809, he advertised in the medical journals his intention of publishing a treatise on some practical points relating to the diseases of the eye, and particularly on the nature and cure of cataract in persons born blind.

Up to the beginning of the nineteenth century only two forms of operation for cataract were in vogue: that of displacing the opaque lens downwards with a needle out of the axis of vision, the operation of " couching," which may be regarded as one of the most ancient of surgical procedures; and that of removal of the opaque lens out of the eye, the operation of " extraction," first performed by the French surgeon Daviel in 1745.

It was observed by several operators who couched cataracts that if they failed in displacing the lens down it was sometimes possible to break it up with the needle, and that the fragments so formed tended in time to disappear. Percival Pott, a surgeon at St. Bartholomew's Hospital, in 1775, first pointed out that this disappearance of the fragments of lens substance was due to them becoming dissolved in the fluids of the eye, and he advocated a procedure to facilitate their solution.

To Conradi, a surgeon at Nordheim in Hanover, seems to be due the merit of first proposing a distinct method of operating for cataract by its division with a needle through the cornea, and he published an account of his method in 1797.

Neither the operation of couching nor that of extraction were found suitable for small children afflicted with cataract, and it was customary in cases of congenital cataract to advise postponement of operation until the patient had arrived at the more manageable age of twelve to fourteen. As has been already mentioned, James Ware, in 1801, contributed a paper to the Royal Society, describing how he had removed a cataract from a boy, aged seven, by breaking it up with a couching needle.

In the medical report of the Dispensary at the end of its second year it is recorded that three children born blind with cataract had been cured at the respective ages of seven, five, and four years. On its receipt by the Governors the following resolution was passed:

" That the thanks of this General Meeting be given to Mr. Saunders for the ability and care by which he has cured so great a number of patients, many of them labouring under the most complicated diseases of the eye, and more especially for having been the first to establish by repeated success the propriety of performing the operation for the cataract at the earliest ages in children born blind of that disease."

So pleased were the Governors with this proof of the value of their charitable institution that they directed that these three small children whose sight had been restored should be introduced at the anniversary dinner. These anniversary dinners were held each year for the purpose of increasing the number of subscribers to the Charity. The dinner at which these children were exhibited was held at the London Tavern, Bishopsgate Street, in May, 1807, at 5 p.m. It is recorded that the price of the dinner was 7s. per head, including beer, bread, cheese, and radishes. The dessert was 1s. 6d. extra, and the wines, port and sherry. The President, Sir Charles Price, Bart., M.P., was in the chair, and about one hundred gentlemen were present; sixty new subscribers were obtained.

At a similar dinner held in the following year the number of Governors and their friends who attended was 277, and new subscriptions to the amount of £708 15s. were received.

In a letter to the Committee, dated March, 1808, Saunders wrote as follows with reference to his work in connection with congenital cataract:

" By the adaptation of an operation on the cataract to the condition of childhood I have successively cured without a failure fourteen persons born blind, some of them even in infancy, and it has just been performed on an infant only two months old who is in a state of convalescence. As I reserve for another occasion the communication of the method which I pursue for the cure of very young children, I shall no further compare it with extraction, than by observing that extraction is wholly inapplicable to children, or only fortuitously successful. Those who on all occasions adhere to this operation, and have never turned their thoughts towards the application of means more suitable to this tender age, have been obliged to wait until the patient has acquired sufficient reason to be tractable; otherwise when they have deviated from this conduct, the event has afforded little cause of self-congratulation.

" How great the advantage of an early cure is a question of no difficult solution. Eyes originally affected with cataracts contract an unsteady and rolling motion, which remains after their removal, and retards, even when it does not ultimately prevent, the full benefit of the operation. A person cured at a late period cannot overcome this awkward habit by the utmost exertion of reason or efforts of the will. But the actions of infants are instinctive. Surrounding objects attract attention, and the eye naturally follows them. The management of the eye is therefore readily acquired, his vision rapidly improves, and he will most probably be susceptible of education about the usual period."

During 1809 Saunders, in preparation for the publication of his advertised treatise, wrote essays " On the Inflammation of the Conjunctiva in Infants " and " On the Cure of the Inversion of the Eyelids by Excision of the Tarsus." He also commenced to put together his notes on congenital cataracts and of his methods of operating on them. His work, however, in these matters became much impeded by recurrent, violent, acute attacks of headache due to brain disease, which in February of the following year proved fatal.

Saunders had realised that congenital cataracts varied considerably in character and consistency, and also that they might be dealt with either by passing the needle, as in couching, through the sclerotic and behind the iris in its approach to the pupillary area, or through the cornea, the so-called anterior operation. He was wisely waiting to gain experience as to which form of procedure was better suited for the different forms of cataract before rushing into print on the matter. He had two pupils working with him at the Dispensary, both of whom subsequently became ophthalmic surgeons, and both of whom in later years wrote in glowing appreciation of all they learnt from him. The one was William (afterwards Sir William) Adams, and the other John Stevenson. Two letters addressed to the latter in April and August, 1808, are the only authentic documents in Saunders' writing descriptive of his operation for cataract; with the first he enclosed two of his improved needles for Stevenson's own use. Needles of a similar pattern are still employed, and known by Saunders' name, at the present time.

" MY DEAR FRIEND,

" I confide the method of operating which I pursue
for cataract to your honour, and I am very certain that it is
safely deposited. I shall not have time to point out all the
advantages which result from this deviation from the old
method of couching; but simple as they appear, they are
very important, as you will perceive when I detail all the
circumstances, which I shall sometime do, in a treatise on the
cataract.

" I always use the solution of Belladonna, and never begin
the operation until the pupil is as much dilated as it will
admit of, keeping the eye, by means of Pellier's elevator, or
else my own fingers, as steady as possible. The object of my
introducing the instrument into the eye is, to cut the capsule
in the anterior part of the crystalline; and therefore, as the
lens is generally more dense towards the centre, I take care
that it shall pass through the crystalline as near to the capsule
as possible. That the instrument may traverse the lens
freely, you will observe that it is made of the greatest tenuity,
and flat, and that it cuts towards the point on each side. I
find by experience that it can be conducted, with care,
through the hardest lens; whereas the needles, such as
Scarpa's and Hey's, only push the whole lens before them,
and without being able to carry the instrument to the capsule,
the lens is made to press on and protrude the iris; whence
results the consequent inflammation. As for the crystalline
itself, you may or may not meddle with that; it may be well
to loosen its texture in some instances, but you ought never
to depress it. . . .

" The instrument should enter the sclerotica about a line
behind the ciliary ligament, and should be conducted through
the anterior part of the crystalline which is softest. You
may loosen the texture of the cataract before you divide the
capsule, or after, as in the operation seems most convenient,
but the *capsule must be divided at all events*. I do not much
care what becomes of the substance of the crystalline. I
sometimes let it go in considerable quantity into the anterior
chamber, if it seems tending that way, but I never push it,
because that must press the iris. *N.B.*—Follow Hey's rule,
to be careful not to do too much. After the operation the
plan with me is purely antiphlogistic, and I believe you
well know what that is. If your operation should not
succeed at the first attempt, describe to me the appear-

ances, and I will gladly give you my sentiments as to repeating it.

" With respect to congenital cataracts, from the repeated conversations we have had on the subject, it seems scarcely necessary for me to remind you, that they are generally capsular, the whole or greater part of the lens having probably been, at some antecedent period during the fœtal state, spontaneously absorbed. I shall only add to what I have already stated, that the steps to be pursued in the operation are nearly similar to those adopted for lenticular cataract; the great object being either to make a sufficiently large central aperture for the rays of light to pass freely through it to the retina, or also to endeavour to tear the condensed capsule into as small fragments as possible, and be gradually absorbed; for which purpose, you may use the needle with much more freedom than in the former case.

" With our united regards,

" I am yours faithfully,

" J. C. SAUNDERS."

It is interesting to note how in these pre-anæsthetic days the small children were kept sufficiently still to allow of operations for cataract to be performed on their eyes. The following is the description of the method employed given by Dr. Farre:

" Four assistants, and in stouter children five, are required to confine the patient. The first fixes the head with reversed hands, the second not only depresses the lower lid with his forefinger, but also receives the chin of the child between his thumb and forefinger, as in a crutch. By this means the play of the head on the breast is prevented, a motion which the child incessantly attempts, and which will very much embarrass the surgeon. The third assistant confines the upper extremities and body; the fourth the lower extremities. The surgeon, seated on a high chair behind the patient, takes Pellier's elevator in his left hand, and the needle in his right, if he is about to operate on the right eye, or the speculum in his right hand and the needle in his left, if the operation is to be performed on the left eye."

The following is the commencement of an unfinished medical report which Saunders had in preparation to present to the Committee of the Infirmary at the time of his death.

" GENTLEMEN,

" Five years have now passed since my proposal for establishing this Infirmary was submitted to your notice, during which I have incessantly and anxiously laboured to redeem the pledge then given to make it a beneficial Institution to Society. My anxiety has been relieved, and my labour consoled in the progress of this Institution, by repeated instances of your respect; and the recollection of them at present only heightens the satisfaction I feel, on finding myself confirmed as the conductor of an establishment supported by liberal and zealous advocates, and possessed of the means of performing an important part in Society, and esteemed by Society for it.

" In prosecuting the object of attracting public attention towards this Institution, I trust I have kept free from the practice of any disingenuous art. Popularity has not been snatched; but studiously and unremittingly sought: it was expected only as a reward of service; and the share of it which has been gained, is ascribable to the estimation in which the Governors have been pleased to hold this service. I have confided the character of the Institution to the quantum of professional good—excepting you may be pleased to add, that mindful of being an agent for liberal and philanthropic men, I have always administered with humanity and attention to the feelings of the poor that relief which their bounty has supplied."

Owing to the early death of Saunders, before the publication of his promised book on diseases of the eye, and of any description of his operation for cataract, there was much heated controversy for many years afterwards, in which the Committee of Management of the Infirmary became involved.

The chief matters around which dispute arose were: the publication of Saunders' unfinished manuscripts; his claim to having introduced a new form of treatment for cataract; the advertisement of his successful results prior to making known to the profession his method of procedure; and the priority of his invention of an operation for the restoration of sight in those in whom it had become impaired from Egyptian ophthalmia.

Saunders died intestate, and there was nothing left for his widow but what might result from the publication of his unfinished manuscripts. The Governors of the Institution decided, in the first instance, that the book should be published at its expense, and that the proceeds of the work (without any deduction) should be appropriated to the sole use and benefit of Mrs. Saunders. It was afterwards found that Mr. Saunders' brother and sister could claim legal rights to the proceeds. It was, therefore, decided in lieu to present £50 to Mrs. Saunders and an annuity of £40. Dr. Farre, at the request of the widow and of Mr. Saunders' brother, consented to edit the book and make good its deficiencies, and it was published by Messrs. Longman and Company in 1811, delay being caused in connection with the question of copyright. Eighteen months after Saunders' death his widow married again, under which circumstances the Committee considered they had reserved to themselves the right of reconsidering her annuity, and it was discontinued. It was agreed, however, that she should retain the copyright of her late husband's book and receive any further proceeds that might arise from its sale; these rights she later parted with to Messrs. Longman and Company for the sum of £50. When a second edition of the book was called for, Longmans offered the copyright to Dr. Farre; he refused it for himself, but accepted it on behalf of the Infirmary. The discontinuance of the annuity to Saunders' widow after her second marriage was the subject of an attack by those at enmity with Farre and Battley up to the time of her death in 1817.

The book, entitled *A Treatise on some Practical Points relating to the Diseases of the Eye*, opens with a short account of Saunders' life, a rather detailed account of his last illness, and a statement of the morbid appearances found by Astley Cooper on the examination of his body. The account of his illness suggests that he suffered from a tumour of the brain, which had affected one of his optic nerves and caused impairment of the sight of his right eye. At the post-mortem examination, however, no tumour was found, the immediate cause of death being cerebral hæmorrhage.

The first two chapters of the book consist of the three previously published essays already referred to; the other three of unfinished notes which were arranged and added to by Dr. Farre, and which deal with " Cases illustrating Changes of Structure in the Eye," and with " Congenital Cataract."

In the course of events it not infrequently happens that circumstances lead up to an epoch when some new development becomes ripe for discovery, and that then more than one mind independently " hits the moment " at about the same time. Later on, when history steps in to record the event, considerable discussion is liable to arise as to whom the palm of priority is to be awarded. This is what occurred in connection with the introduction of the operation of solution for the removal of congenital cataracts.

The solubility of the substance of the crystalline lens in the aqueous humour of the eye had been recognised long before Saunders began to operate for cataract. But in introducing the method of solution for the dispersion of cataracts in infancy he undoubtedly believed he had discovered a new method of treatment. He appears to have been unaware of Conradi's method of needling cataracts in adults, published in Germany. The real value of his contribution to ophthalmology in this matter is well estimated in the following extract from a lecture published in the *Lancet* by Mr. Green, a surgeon at St. Thomas's Hospital, in 1823:

" I do not mean to say that this operation is entirely new; if you read Mr. Pott's works, you will find that, in some instances, he performed a very similar operation. He tells you, that in cases where the cataract was too soft for depression, he sometimes lacerated the anterior layers of the capsule, so as to admit the aqueous humour, and procure the solution of the cataract. Hey, Scarpa, and Ware have performed similar operations. We are not, however, to consider those as inventors of any practice who have merely employed it here and there, without stating any certain rules for its general applicability. It is to Dr. Saunders that we are indebted for having shown the principle on which he performed this particular operation, its applicability to cataract in children, and to some cases of cataract in adults. Dr. Saunders, therefore, may be justly considered as the inventor of this operation, and entitled to our respect and admiration of so material an improvement in this branch of surgery."

It must, however, be admitted that it was an error of judgment on Saunders' part to have allowed the Committee of Management to advertise in the public press, stating that operations were being performed at the Infirmary on children born blind of cataract, before the nature of the operation had been made known to the medical profession. Such a practice, together with the exhibition of the children who had been operated on at a public dinner, savoured rather of the methods of the quack oculists, though Saunders himself derived no pecuniary benefit and died a poor man.

Benjamin Gibson in Manchester, independently of Saunders, recognised the possibility of operating successfully on congenital cataracts in infancy, and in the October number, for 1811, of the *Edinburgh Medical and Surgical Journal*, published a description of his methods in an article entitled " On the Use of the Couching-needle in Infants of a Few Months Old." The description of his operation was, therefore, published almost at the same time as Dr. Farre's description of Saunders' methods of procedure.

Saunders' two pupils, William Adams (afterwards Sir William) and John Stevenson, followed the example of their teacher, both claiming to having introduced new methods of operating on the eye, and both founding institutions for the treatment of its diseases.

William Adams, as already mentioned, had, like Saunders, served his apprenticeship with John Hill, of Barnstaple, and had completed his medical education at St. Thomas's and Guy's Hospitals. He worked under Saunders in the dissecting room and also at the Eye Infirmary, assisting him for a year and a half in both his public and private operations. After obtaining the diploma M.R.C.S. in 1807, he went to reside in Exeter, where he founded the West of England Eye Infirmary for curing diseases of the eye, on the same lines as the one in London; this Institution continues its work to-day under the same name. To it Saunders allowed his name to be attached as Consulting Surgeon, and wrote advice on several occasions to Adams concerning his work there.

Saunders had pledged Adams not to reveal the nature of the operations he had learnt from him before he had had time to publish a description of them. Even before Saunders' death Adams resented being bound to observe this pledge, and after his death considered himself exonerated from its further observance. Most operators in the course of their practice introduce modifications in their procedures. Adams considered that the modifications which he introduced in the operations he had learnt from Saunders justified him in claiming them as his own. It was on the strength of these claims, that on his return to London, after Saunders' death in 1810, he was appointed to operate on pensioners dismissed from the Army as blind through Egyptian ophthalmia. The operation he performed was a modification of that introduced by Saunders of excision of the tarsus of the eyelid. He was also appointed to operate for cataract on seamen at Greenwich, and later an Ophthalmic Institution was founded for him in part of the York Hospital, Chelsea, which was afterwards transferred to Regent's Park.

He became oculist extraordinary to the Prince Regent and to the Dukes of Kent and Sussex, and in 1814 was knighted. A Select Committee of Parliament reported on his work at the Ophthalmic Institution and on his claim to public money, and with Lord Palmerston's support he was voted the sum of £4,000.

Sir William Adams' claims to the invention of new operative procedures was much resented by Farre and Battley, who regarded them as piracy of their deceased friend's work at the Eye Infirmary. In 1814 the Committee of Management of that Institution requested its medical directors to furnish them with a report on the matter, showing how Sir William Adams' claims had been anticipated. This report was sent to His Royal Highness the Duke of York, the Commander-in-Chief of the Army, and to His Majesty's Ministers, with the request that deputations from those connected with the Infirmary might be received. As an outcome of the deputation to the Duke of York, His Royal Highness graciously condescended to become a Patron of the Infirmary.

In 1817, when the question of a monetary grant to Sir William Adams was raised in Parliament, further deputations waited on Lord Palmerston and on the Chancellor of the Exchequer with the object of refuting his claims, and of obtaining some pecuniary assistance for the Infirmary's building fund, but no success in the latter direction was met with.

In later life Adams became interested in Anglo-Mexican mines, but his speculations do not appear to have been attended with success. Two years before his death he changed his name to Rawson in compliance with the will of his wife's mother, the widow of Colonel Rawson.*

John Stevenson, like Adams, worked under Saunders in the dissecting room at St. Thomas's Hospital and at the Eye

* It is due to this change of name that a writer of a life of Sir William Adams, in Vol. II. of the *British Journal of Ophthalmology*, failed to find a notice of him in the *Dictionary of National Biography*. It is from the description there given of Sir William Rawson that most of the above facts respecting him have been taken.

Infirmary. Having obtained the diploma of M.R.C.S., he settled in or near Nottingham, but on Saunders' death returned to London to practise there as an oculist and aurist. In 1813 he was appointed as such to the Prince of Wales and to Leopold, the Duke of Saxe-Coburg.

He wrote several treatises on the structure and functions of the eye and ear, and much on the subject of cataract and its treatment. Whilst always acknowledging his obligations to Saunders and his admiration for his genius and industry, he claimed credit for having introduced a method of successfully removing cataracts in adults at an earlier stage in their development than was then usual, and thereby obviating a prolonged period of semi-blindness.

In 1830 he founded at 13, Little Portland Street, Cavendish Square, the Royal Infirmary for Cataract and other Diseases of the Eye, under the Patronage of His Majesty King William IV., to whom he was soon after appointed oculist and aurist. This Infirmary, besides the patronage of the King, had a long list of Royal Patronesses and of noble supporters. The indigent poor suffering from all forms of diseases of the eye were treated gratis as out-patients, but only cataract cases were admitted as in-patients. In the *Dictionary of National Biography* it is stated that after 1844 all trace of Stevenson is lost.

It is noteworthy that both this Infirmary and Wathen's Institution, which were established under Royal Patronage in the West End of London, existed for only a comparatively brief time; whilst that founded by Saunders, with the approval and support of the medical and surgical staffs of the Borough Hospitals, and under the patronage of the City fathers, has continued to flourish and grow in the manner which the following pages will relate.

Farre described Saunders as a man of middle size, well made and of an engaging mien, with an active mind, generous in his private practice, and perfectly unreserved in stating his opinion in cases submitted to his judgment. That he had the capacity of forming firm friendships is shown by the marked respect which Farre describes as having been paid to him at his funeral, and the steps which were taken to perpetuate his memory.   At a General Meeting of the Governors of the Eye Infirmary it was unanimously agreed that a portrait and bust of Mr. Saunders should be obtained and placed in the Committee Room.   In accordance with this resolution a portrait was painted by Devis, and a bust was executed by Henry Weekes.   The former hangs to-day in the Board Room of the present Hospital, and an engraving of it by Anthony Cardon was inserted as a frontispiece to Saunders' treatise, and is still used to adorn the certificates which are presented to students who have completed a course of instruction at the Hospital.

This portrait shows Saunders with a mass of brown curly hair coming low down over his forehead, with mutton-chop whiskers, pronounced features and a mouth shaped like a Cupid's bow.   He wears a high white stock round his neck, has a frill to his shirt, and a blue coat.

CHAPTER III

BENJAMIN TRAVERS AND SIR WILLIAM LAWRENCE

THE death of the founder of the Charity only five years after it was first opened placed its Committee of Management in a most difficult and unexpected position. Astley Cooper came to its immediate assistance, conducting the operating department and frequently attending in the receiving room until a new surgeon was appointed. Being keenly interested in all branches of surgery, he was probably pleased to have this opportunity of gaining experience in the surgery of the eye.

The vacancy was advertised in three leading London newspapers, several applications being received in response. Amongst the candidates were Saunders' former pupil at the Infirmary, John Stevenson, and William Lawrence (afterwards Sir William), who was then demonstrator of anatomy at St. Bartholomew's Hospital; both of these, however, withdrew their applications in favour of Benjamin Travers, who was unanimously elected at a ballot of the General Committee.

Benjamin Travers was then twenty-seven years of age, and had been a house pupil of Astley Cooper's, of whom evidently he was a great admirer, for in later years he wrote this description of him:

" Astley Cooper, when I first knew him, had the decidedly handsomest, that is the most intelligent and finely formed, countenance and person of any man I remember to have seen. He wore his hair powdered, with a queue, then the custom, and having dark hair and always a fine, healthy glow in his cheeks, this fashion became him well. His

33

frequent costume during the summer when taking horse exercise (for at this season he rode daily on horseback) was a blue coat, yellow buckskin breeches and top-boots, then much in vogue."

Travers had been articled at the Royal College of Surgeons for six years; he was, therefore, unlike Saunders, eligible for appointment as surgeon to a general hospital when a vacancy arose, and was so appointed to St. Thomas's Hospital in 1815. At the time of Saunders' death he was demonstrator of anatomy at Guy's Hospital and surgeon to the East India Company.

In accepting the post of surgeon to the Eye Infirmary he did not, like Saunders, devote himself exclusively to treating diseases of the eye and ear, but combined the practice of ophthalmic surgery with that of general surgery. In the preface of a book he subsequently wrote, entitled *A Synopsis of Disease of the Eye*, he claims to have been the first general hospital surgeon in this country to have given more than a cursory attention to diseases of the eye. In doing so he incurred no small risk to his reputation as a general surgeon, for, as already stated, those who practised as oculists at that time were of but low repute. His courageous and disinterested action in this matter served, however, to raise the surgery of the eye out of the condition of quackery into which it had fallen.

Shortly after Travers was appointed surgeon to the Infirmary it was decided to increase its accommodation by providing eight additional beds, so that other than cataract cases might be admitted.

In 1811, in accordance with the recommendation of Dr. Farre and Mr. Travers, the practice of the Infirmary was opened to medical students, and permission was granted to the medical officers to deliver lectures on the subject of their profession. Thus was started the school of ophthalmology which has since developed into a teaching centre of worldwide renown.

PLATE III.

SIR ASTLEY PASTON COOPER, BART., F.R.S.

From an engraving by W. H. Mote, after a picture by Sir T. Lawrence, P.R.A.

[To face p 34

Amongst the earliest students to avail themselves of the instruction given were two young Americans, who had recently graduated in medicine at the College of Physicians and Surgeons in New York, and who had come to London to complete their training: Dr. Edward Delafield and Dr. J. Kearney Rodgers. So impressed were they with the Institution and its teaching that, on their return to New York in 1818, they determined to establish one on similar lines in that city. In August, 1820, " The New York Eye and Ear Infirmary " was opened, and continues as one of the leading special hospitals of the sort in America at the present time. It is interesting to note that whilst the parent Institution has changed its title from that of " Infirmary " to that of " Hospital," the daughter Institutions both in Exeter and New York retain the older name.

Dr. Delafield later showed his appreciation of Travers' teaching by editing an edition of his *Synopsis of Diseases of the Eye*, which was published in New York. As one of the first surgeons in the United States to devote himself to the study of diseases of the eye, he was, when the American Ophthalmological Society was founded in 1864, most appropriately elected its first President.

A few years later Dr. Edward Reynolds came from Boston, Mass., to London to pursue his medical studies. He attended the practice and lectures at the Eye Infirmary under Benjamin Travers and William Lawrence, and, in a letter written home to Dr. J. C. Warren, gave the following description of the former:

" He is not a very pleasant lecturer—his voice is low and his manner is very inanimate and uninteresting, but his matter, however, is very valuable."

On Dr. Reynolds' return from Europe he found his father blind from cataract in both eyes. There were no specialists in that part of the country at that time, so, fortified by his recent experiences in London, he decided to operate, happily with complete success. The following is an interesting description of this event, written by Dr. Edward Reynolds grandson in 1910:·

" I well remember my grandfather's telling me of his operation on his father's eye. He told me that his father, finding his eyesight failing, made great efforts to accustom himself to its gradual disappearance and to the performance of his ordinary duties without the aid of sight, and that upon one occasion, after finishing the process of shaving between two windows in his room, he put away his razor and, turning to his wife, said to her: ' My dear, I am at last totally blind, I can see nothing.' My grandfather said that his father had written him nothing of this infirmity, which came on while he was a student in London; that it was, in consequence, a great shock to him to find his father blind. He said that on looking at the eyes, and satisfying himself that the blindness was due to cataracts, he thought the situation over; that his father was too old to take the sailing voyage to London and, so far as he knew, no operation for cataracts had been performed in America, and certainly none in this locality; that he was therefore probably better qualified than any one available for the performance of the operation; and that he decided to attempt it. He said: ' I went into my closet and offered a prayer to Deity for success, took a glass of sherry and went ahead to do my best.' The three phrases of this sentence have always seemed to me exceedingly characteristic of the man as I knew him."

The success of the operation becoming widely known led to the foundation of Dr. Reynolds' reputation as the leading surgeon in Boston in diseases of the eye, and to the foundation in 1824 of " The Massachusetts Charitable Eye and Ear Infirmary."

As already mentioned, Travers held the appointment of surgeon in London to the East India Company. In 1819 its Honourable Directors became impressed by the great prevalence of eye disease in the large and populous districts over which they ruled, and applied to Travers in the matter. He pointed out to them the excellent results which had followed the establishment of the Eye Infirmary in London, and that similar Institutions might be started in India. This advice was accepted, and Mr. R. Richardson, one of the Company's surgeons, who had studied ophthalmology under Travers, was sent to Madras, where he founded " The Madras Eye Infirmary," which was each year resorted to by increasing numbers of patients. The Infirmary has been several times enlarged, and in 1888 its name was altered to that by which it is now known, " The Government Ophthalmic Hospital."

Stimulated by the success which attended the establishment of the Eye Infirmary in Madras, the East India Company determined to start similar Institutions in other provinces. In 1824 two other surgeons who had studied at the London Eye Infirmary were sent out to India for this purpose: Mr. Jeafferson went to Bombay and Mr. C. J. Egerton to Calcutta, where each of them founded an Eye Hospital.

During the first seven years that the London Eye Infirmary was open for medical students 412 pupils received instruction there, of whom fifty were physicians and the rest surgeons. They came not only from the three divisions of the United Kingdom, but also from India, America, Germany, Portugal, and other countries; many of them held important posts in the Army and Navy. Ten years later still it is recorded that the number who had received instruction at the Institution considerably exceeded one thousand, and that they were spread over every part of the world.

In 1814 Travers found the increasing number of patients coming to the Infirmary made the work so arduous that it was impossible for one individual to cope with it satisfactorily, and he wrote to the Committee requesting them to appoint a second surgeon to co-operate with him. This they readily agreed to, and, at a meeting of the General Committee, with whom the election of members of the medical staff then rested, William Lawrence, demonstrator of anatomy and assistant surgeon to St. Bartholomew's Hospital, was appointed.

One of Travers' earliest surgical achievements was the cure of a pulsating tumour of the orbit, described as an aneurism by anastomosis, by ligature of the common carotid artery. It was the first case in which such treatment had been employed, and the second case on record of successful ligature of that artery. He communicated the case to the newly formed Medico-Chirurgical Society in 1809. He was possessed of considerable literary ability, and rendered Sir Astley Cooper considerable assistance in collaborating with him in the production of a volume of surgical essays. In 1815 Travers was elected a Fellow of the Royal Society, and in 1820, after he had resigned his appointment at the London Eye Infirmary, published the treatise already referred to, entitled *A Synopsis of Diseases of the Eye*, which he dedicated to Dr. J. R. Farre, in esteem for his character, admiration of his talents, and gratitude for his friendship. This book had the merit of being entirely the outcome of his own observations at the Eye Infirmary, and was not a compilation of the work of others. It is stated to have been the application of Hunterian principles of inflammation to the diseases of the eye. That it met with a wide appreciation is shown by its having passed through three editions, by its having been translated into Italian, and by its being re-edited and reproduced in New York by Travers' former pupil, Dr. Delafield.

From a writer of an obituary notice we get the following description of Travers as a man:

" He was tall, large formed, and well proportioned, with a highly intelligent and pleasing countenance. His manners were prepossessing, and in consultation with his professional brethren he showed a high-bred courtesy which marked the refinement of his mind."

Pressure of work, and some fears as to his health, necessitated his retirement from the staff of the Eye Infirmary

PLATE IV.

BENJAMIN TRAVERS, F.R.S.

[To face p. 38

in 1817. He lived, however, until 1858, and was twice elected President of the Royal College of Surgeons. The year before his death he was appointed serjeant surgeon to Queen Victoria.

The chief financial support of the Infirmary for many years after its foundation was derived from subscriptions and donations received at its anniversary dinners. The exhibition of patients at these dinners was apparently continued until 1812, for a minute of that year states that their attendance was in future to be dispensed with.

Another method of raising funds in support of the Charity was to obtain the services of some eminent divine to preach a sermon on its behalf on the Sunday before the dinner, with permission for him to do so at one of the City churches. Alderman Ansley, who had been one of the Infirmary's most jealous supporters since its conception, in the year of his Mayoralty, not only presided at its annual meeting of Governors and at the anniversary dinner, but also attended in state at Bow Church when the Rev. Henry White preached a sermon in support of the Charity.

It is interesting further to note that, in spite of the Peninsular War, which is said to have cost England £100,000,000, and of the European campaign which followed Napoleon's escape from Elba and ended with the Battle of Waterloo, the funds of the Charity showed a steady increase, both that for general purposes and one started in 1813 for purchase of a freehold and the erection of a suitable building. In 1815, the Waterloo year, the anniversary dinner was held in May, presided over by the President, Sir Charles Price, Bart., and the anniversary sermon was preached at St. Botolph's, Aldersgate Street, before the Lord Mayor. The invested fund for general purposes in April that year amounted to £2,415, and the building fund to £852; in October the general purposes fund had increased to £2,800 and the building fund to £1,160.

The rapid increase in the work of the Infirmary, both in

the in- and out-patients' departments, necessitated in 1816
a reorganization of its resident staff, and it was arranged
that this should consist of a housekeeper and sister with
a salary of 25 guineas per annum, a housemaid at 10 guineas,
a cook at 12 guineas and a resident apothecary and sub-
secretary at £50 per annum.   A year previously a dispenser
had been appointed to make up and distribute drugs for the
patients in place of Mr. Clarke, the porter; it was now decided
that these duties should be performed by a resident officer.
From the rules drawn up detailing the apothecary's duties,
they would seem to have included all those now performed
by the house surgeons, dispensers, and the assistant secretary.

His first and most important occupation is defined as
follows:

" To compound and dispense the medicines, to cup,
bleed, apply leeches, dress setons, etc., and to obey orders
of the Medical Directors relative to the business of the
Infirmary."

The withdrawal of blood was regarded at that time as of
the utmost importance for the reduction of inflammatory
conditions of the eye, and the apothecary must have had his
time fully occupied in this way.   Respecting the general
principles for its employment, Lawrence wrote:

" Of the means of reducing inflammation, abstraction of
blood is the most powerful.   Blood is the material by which
the increasing action of the part is maintained.   In the
figurative language, which the obviously increased heat has
suggested, we may say that it is the fuel by which the fire
is kept up.   If we could completely command the supply of
blood, the increased action might be effectively controlled
or arrested.   In comparison with the loss of blood, all other
means are of minor importance in lessening the local dis-
order and quieting the general disturbance."

Regarding the quantity of blood to be drawn from the arm,
he says:

" We cannot determine the amount beforehand; we cannot decide that ten, twelve, or sixteen ounces will be sufficient; it may be necessary to take twenty, thirty, or forty ounces, or to produce syncope, if you cannot otherwise make the requisite impression on the vascular system."

After venesection the next best method of taking blood is:

" By cupping from the back of the neck or the temple, especially the latter, from which blood can be obtained quickly and in large quantity. Branches of the temporal artery are commonly wounded in this operation, facilitating the abstraction of the blood, and causing neither danger nor inconvenience."

With regard to the use of leeches he writes:

" It is a common error here, as in other inflammations, to apply them in too small a number; if the disease be active and the patient adult, it will seldom be proper to put on fewer than twelve, while eighteen or twenty-four will more frequently be necessary, in order to produce decided benefit."

In a book published " on the traffic with leeches " in 1826, it is stated that not less than seven million two hundred thousand of these animals were annually sent to England.

This so-called " antiphlogistic treatment," which was so implicitly relied upon in those times for the relief of inflammation in the eye, consisted, not only in the withdrawal of blood, but also in purging, dieting and the administration of tartar emetic to excite perspiration, nausea, or vomiting. Lawrence writes:

" It is not sufficient in the treatment of inflammation to diminish the quantity of the circulating fluid by the abstraction of blood, we must prevent the introduction of further supplies into the vascular system by the use of purgatives and the regulation of diet."

The diet of the patients in the Infirmary, from the table then in use, seems, according to our present standards, to have been both meagre and monotonous. It was arranged

under three headings, " Low diet "; " Reduced diet ";
and " Full diet." Low diet consisted of milk pottage or
gruel, with 12 oz. of bread for women, and 1 lb. for men.
Reduced diet consisted of the same allowance of bread, but
included broth in addition to milk pottage. Full diet had,
in addition to the milk pottage and bread, 8 oz. of meat,
broth and vegetables for dinner, and one pint of small beer.

In 1817 new regulations were drawn up for the election
of medical officers. The qualifications required of candidates for the offices of physician, surgeon, and apothecary
were as follows: *Physician:* that he be a Fellow or Licentiate
of the London College of Physicians, or a Bachelor of
Medicine of one of the English Universities. *Surgeon:*
that he be a Member of the College of Surgeons, and have
served an apprenticeship at one of the hospitals of this
Metropolis. *Apothecary:* that he be a Member of the
College of Surgeons, and a Licentiate of the Society of
Apothecaries. It was further arranged that the election of
medical officers should be vested in the Governors, and not
left to the General Committee, as was previously the case.

After these regulations had been passed Travers resigned
the post of surgeon, which he had held for seven years, and
was elected a Vice-President. It had been a source of great
satisfaction to him to have had a man of William Lawrence's
professional attainments appointed as his colleague on the
staff. In the year previous to his joining the Infirmary Lawrence had been elected a Fellow of the Royal Society, and
appointed assistant-surgeon to St. Bartholomew's Hospital.
Travers felt that, with Lawrence's co-operation, his unprecedented step of associating the practice of an oculist with
that of a general surgeon was being justified. The Infirmary
also gained a better reputation in the profession, by showing
that it was not merely the offshoot of one hospital, but was
prepared to appoint as members of its staff those educated
at, and connected with, other institutions.

William Lawrence not only became the leading ophthalmic

surgeon of his time, but also a leading general surgeon, a philosophic writer, an eloquent teacher and lecturer, and a strongly combative medical politician. It is unnecessary here to go into the inconsistencies in his career, such as the withdrawal from publication of his book on the *Comparative Anatomy, Physiology, Zoology, and Natural History of Man*, when it aroused an angry outcry from the orthodox religious folk of the day; and his change from being a leading reformer of the constitution of the College of Surgeons to one of its most vigorous supporters. In his recognition of the importance of a knowledge of diseases of the eye by medical men he always remained firm, being the first to advocate that a course of instruction in it should be included in the medical curriculum.

In an introductory chapter to his *Treatise on Diseases of the Eye*, he urged that the course of procedure in the study of ophthalmology should be the same as that for diseases in general, and be founded on the science of anatomy, physiology, pathology, and therapeutics. He pointed out that the instruction given at the Eye Infirmary was intended to impart to physicians and surgeons a knowledge of ophthalmic disease, and not merely to make oculists.

In this same introductory chapter he gives a short history of ophthalmology, from which some points may here be quoted. Amongst the ancient Egyptians there were specialists for affections of the eye, as there were for every other class of disease. Herodotus tells us that Cyrus, King of Persia, sent to Amasis, King of Egypt, for an oculist. The extent of the Greeks' knowledge of eye disease is evidenced by the imperishable records of language, for many of them still bear the names given to them by the ancient Greek writers· That the Roman Emperors Augustus and Tiberius had oculists is evident from inscriptions on seals. In the fifteenth, sixteenth, seventeenth, and first half of the eighteenth centuries, the management of diseases of the eye was left to quacks, mountebanks, and itinerant practitioners, the French writers on the subject, Maître-Jan, St. Yves, and Janin, being more respectable than their contemporary brethren in other countries. The anatomy of the organ began to be more carefully cultivated by the Germans about the middle of the eighteenth century, when Zinn, Professor of Anatomy at Göttingen, published his excellent *Descriptio Anatomic Oculi Humani*, and later Soemerring his *Icones Oculi Humani*, with its beautiful and accurate engravings. Boerhaave of Leyden made some study of the pathology of the eye in his *De Morbus Oculorum*. But the most important era in the history of ophthalmic surgery was the establishment of the Vienna school of ophthalmology in 1773, by Joseph Barth, who was appointed lecturer on ophthalmic surgery in the University of Vienna in that year. He was succeeded by Schmidt, and afterwards by Beer, who held the post of Professor of Ophthalmic Medicine in the University for many years, wrote several theses on the subject, and attracted students to his clinic from all parts of Europe.

If a man's worth is to be judged by the estimates of those who were his pupils and assistants, then indeed Sir William Lawrence must be described as great. Sir James Paget, who in his day was the most fluent and mellifluous orator in the medical profession, said in describing Lawrence's teaching:

" It was the best method of scientific speaking that I ever heard, and there was no one, at that time in England, if I may not say in Europe, who had more completely studied the whole principle and practice of surgery."

Sir William Savory, Lawrence's most devoted disciple, who described him as "a model of intellectual beauty," speaks of

" his natural grace and dignity of bearing," of " his vast and capacious intellect," of " his unfailing fluency of pure and perspicuous language," and says " he touched nothing that he did not adorn."

PLATE V.

SIR WILLIAM LAWRENCE BART., F.R.S.
From an engraving by E. R. Whitfield, after a picture by Pickersgill, R.A.

[To face p. 44

On the vacancy on the staff being advertised after Travers' retirement, applications were received from Edward Stanley, a former pupil at the Infirmary, who was then demonstrator of anatomy at St. Bartholomew's Hospital; Frederick Tyrrell, who had served his apprenticeship under Sir Astley Cooper at Guy's and St. Thomas's Hospitals, who had also studied at Edinburgh University, and worked in the Military Hospital at Brussels after Waterloo; Samuel Cooper, whose name is famous in connection with his *Dictionary of Surgery*; Henry Earle, surgeon of the Foundling Hospital and assistant-surgeon to St. Bartholomew's Hospital.

It soon became evident that the Governors were in favour of a candidate coming from St. Thomas's Hospital, with which Travers, who was retiring, was connected, and the other candidates withdrew their applications, expressing their wish to come forward again on some future occasion, so that Tyrrell was elected.

Lawrence continued as senior surgeon to the Infirmary until 1826, retiring at the age of forty-three. Both he and Dr. Farre were regular attendants at the meetings of the Committee of Management, and lent valuable aid and advice in the arrangements connected with the building of the new Infirmary at Moorfields.

After his retirement he published a book on *The Venereal Diseases of the Eye*. Previous to its appearance, affections of the eye had received but scant attention from writers on venereal diseases in this country, though they had been dealt with more extensively by Schmidt and Beer in Vienna. The former seems to have been the first to describe inflammation of the iris, and to have used the term " iritis."

In the first chapter of the book Lawrence says:

" The venereal diseases of the eye have been mentioned by many writers, but, for the most part, in such general terms as to convey no clear information respecting the circumstances under which they arise, their characteristic appearances, their progress, effects, or treatment. Hence, although one of these affections, namely acute gonorrhœal inflammation of the conjunctiva, is of the most violent and rapidly destructive kind, and another, syphilitic iritis, produces, more or less speedily, changes of structure which injure or destroy sight, they have entirely escaped the notice of some modern writers in this country, who have been regarded as the principal authorities on the venereal diseases."

The book gives a full account of the nature, symptoms, and treatment of these diseases, based entirely on Lawrence's own experience. The notes of the cases from which his descriptions were drawn are appended, most of them having been under his care at the Eye Infirmary, thus bearing evidence to the advantage of a special hospital in supplying material for the study of the natural history of disease.

In 1833 he published his *Treatise on Diseases of the Eye*, a most scholarly work, based, as he says in the advertisement, on the lectures on Anatomy, Physiology, and Diseases of the Eye, which he delivered at the London Ophthalmic Infirmary, and which were reported at the time in the *Lancet*. It contained not only the outcome of his matured experience, but also references to the views and practice of all the best known European writers. It is probably one of the best, if not the best, book dealing with eye disease in pre-ophthalmoscopic times; two further editions were published in England and one in America. It was also translated into several foreign languages, part even into Arabic.

Lawrence continued to hold his post of surgeon to St. Bartholomew's Hospital until 1865, when he retired at the age of eighty-two, no age limit having been fixed previous to his appointment. In 1867 he was appointed serjeant surgeon to Queen Victoria, and in 1867 was made a Baronet, but died the following year.

In 1818 Richard Battley, who had gratuitously performed the duties of secretary to the Institution since its establishment, found it necessary to resign. He did not, however, cease to interest himself in the work of the Charity he had helped to found; he continued to attend its Committees, and, as we shall see later, he taught and lectured to students on matters connected with pharmaceutical subjects.

In the same year the Infirmary lost, through death, two of its earliest and most enthusiastic supporters, its first President, Sir Charles Price, Bart., and the Chairman of its Committee, Mr. Harry Sedgwick. To the post of President thus left vacant Mr. William Mellish, M.P., was elected. The name of Sedgwick is still held in grateful remembrance at the Hospital, and will be as long as it continues, for in his will he provided for its endowment, as is shown by the following extract:

" I leave the interest of the remainder of my Property to my wife and children or the survivors of them for their lives, and to my sister if she survives them for her life. After her decease, I leave in trust the principal, to be invested in the 3 Per Cent. Consols, in the names of the President, Treasurer, Physician, and Surgeon of the London Infirmary for Curing Diseases of the Eyes, now situated in Charterhouse Square, the principal on no account whatever to be touched, but the interest as it arises to be applied to the benefit of that truly benevolent and valuable Institution for ever."

CHAPTER IV

REMOVAL TO MOORFIELDS

THE lease of the house in Charterhouse Square was purchased for a period of eighteen years; at the end of nine years it became obvious that, to cope with the continuously increasing work of the Charity, it would be necessary when the lease expired to provide larger and more commodious premises. It was, therefore, decided in 1813 to open a fund for the provision of a suitable freehold and building. To this fund the Lord Mayor, Aldermen, and Common Council of the City of London, as a mark of their approval, contributed £100.

In March, 1819, a Building Committee was appointed to find a suitable site and to draw up plans. The possibility of acquiring from the City a piece of ground in Moorfields soon came under consideration. Frederick Tyrrell was the son of Timothy Tyrrell, who was the City Remembrancer and resided at the Guildhall, and it was with his aid that negotiations for this site were entered into. Timothy Tyrrell became a member of the General Committee of the Infirmary, and his eldest son, John Tyrrell, a barrister, became an active member of the Building Committee.

Though the option for refusal of a plot of land to the north of the Roman Catholic Chapel in Moorfields was then obtained from the City, it was not until more than a year later that an agreement to acquire the freehold was decided upon. In the meantime, several other possible sites had been inspected and rejected.

It was in October, 1820, that, at a meeting at the Guildhall with the Committee of the City Lands, the following terms were finally entered into:

" That the Infirmary should acquire the freehold of a plot of land on the North-East side of Moorfields, to the extent of 88 ft. in width and 85 ft. in depth, for the sum of £800, to be paid at the time of the roof of the intended building being complete, and that a pepper-corn rent only be paid from Christmas next until Lady Day 1822. The Institution to be at the expense of preparing the Title."

Robert Smirke, F.R.S., F.A.S., R.A. (afterwards Sir Robert), was commissioned to prepare plans for the building, the expenses of which were to be limited to £5,000. Subsequently Smirke found that, in consequence of the unexpected loose nature of the land of the site chosen, extra expense would be incurred in forming the foundations of the proposed building, and the limit of the amount was increased to £5,500.

On May 2nd, 1821, the General Committee of the Infirmary, after having assembled at the City of London Tavern, proceeded with the President to the ground in Moorfields to lay the foundation stone of the new building, in which stone was deposited the following coins: 1 sovereign, 1 half-sovereign, 1 crown, 1 half-crown, of the reign of George IV.; 1 shilling, 1 sixpence, and in silver, one piece value each 4d., 3d., 2d., 1d., of the reign of George III.; upon these was placed a brass plate having the following inscription engraved thereon:

" London Infirmary for Curing Diseases of the Eye, founded by the late John Cunningham Saunders, Esq., A.D. MDCCCIV. The foundation-stone of the new building for the same Institution, henceforth to be entitled The London Ophthalmic Infirmary, was laid in Moorfields, on the second day of May, 1821, by the President.

Patron : Field-Marshal His Royal Highness the Duke of York, K.G., etc.

President : William Mellish, Esq.

Vice-Presidents :

St. Asaph, The Right Rev. Lord Bishop of.
John Ansley, Esq., Ald.
John Julius Angerstein, Esq.
William Babington, M.D., F.R.S.
George Bainbridge, Esq.
Thomas Boddington, Esq.
George Byng, Esq., M.P.
Henry Cline, Esq, F.R.S.
Astley Cooper, Esq., F.R.S.
Sir Charles Flower, Bart.,Ald.
Thos. F. Foster, Esq.
Sir William Leighton, Ald.
Sir Charles Price, Bart.
Jeremiah Olive, Esq.
Thomas Rowcroft, Esq.
Sir James Shaw, Bart., Ald.
John Thompson, Esq.
Benjamin Travers, Esq., F.R.S.
Sir Robert Wingram, Bart.

Treasurer : Michael Bland, Esq., F.R.S.

Medical Directors.

Physician : John Richard Farre, M.D.
Surgeons : William Lawrence, Esq., F.R.S.
Frederick Tyrrell, Esq.

Committee :

Aaron, Lewis, Esq.
Bainbridge, John, Esq.
Bonsor, Joseph, Esq.
Blades, John, Esq.
Brandain, Samuel, Esq.
Brown, Thomas, Esq.
Browning, William, Esq.
Brydon, William, Esq.
Battley, Richard, Esq.
Cazenove, John, Esq.
Clarke, John, Esq.
Cohen, Joseph, Esq.
Crawley, William, Esq.
Croskey, J. D., Esq.
Curtis, Timothy, Esq.
Dean, John, Esq.
Elgie, William, Esq.
Gamble, Robert, Esq.
Hartshorne, John, Esq.
Heathfield, Richard, Esq.
Hodgkinson, John, Esq.
Horner, John, Esq.
Kerr, Niven, Esq.
Mackie, John, Esq.
Mellish, Thos., Esq.
Ommanney, Sir F. M., M.P.
Pearce, J. M., Esq.
Price, Ralph, Esq.
Price, Richard, Esq.
Price, Charles, Esq.
Russell, Rev. John, D.D.
Read, Samuel, Esq.
Row, William, Esq.
Rudge,Rev.Jas.,D.D.,F.R.S.
Smirke, Robert, Esq.
Solly, Thomas, Esq.
Sparks, R. W., Esq.
Towle, Thomas, Esq.
Thomas, John, Esq.
Tyrrell, John, Esq.
Tyrrell, Timothy, Esq.
Warburton, Thos., Esq.
Ward, Samuel, Esq.
Yates, William, Jun., Esq.

Hon. Chaplain : The Rev. Thos. Gill, M.A.
Solicitor : Robert Pitches, Esq.
Secretary : Matthew Heathfield, Esq.
Apothecary : Mr. Charles Craddock.
Architect : Robert Smirke, Esq., F.R.S., F.A.S., R.A."

A prayer suitable to the occasion was offered up to Almighty God by the Chaplain.

At six o'clock the Governors and friends of the Charity dined at the City of London Tavern, when contributions since January 1st of that year were announced to the amount of about £1,200 for the building fund.

Moorfields was originally a piece of moorland lying to the north of the old City wall, access to which was obtained through the Moorgate. Early in the seventeenth century it was drained, laid out in walks, and planted with trees. For a long time it remained a place of recreation and jollification for the City folk—a place of swings and roundabouts, as is described in the following verses in the *vade mecum* for malt worms:

" In Moor's most pleasant Field, where Northern Lads
  With Western Youths contend for broken Heads,
  And where our Weal thy Citizens repair
  To lengthen out their Lives with wholesome Air;
  Jointing to Trotter's famous Castle, stands
  A noted Mansion built by artful Hands;
  Where Young and Old, at small Expense can find
  Delightful Pastimes to refresh the Mind.
  Hither the sprightly Genius has recourse
  To practise Riding on the Flying-Horse;
  Where danger-free, he through the Air may scow'r,
  And, void the Wings, fly fifty miles an Hour;
  Nor that has this Courser, tho' he runs so fast,
  One living Leg to expediate him hast,
  Yet carries double, treble, if requir'd,
  But never stumbles or is ever tir'd.
  As for the pregnant Wife, or tim'rous Maid,
  Here's a true South-Sea Coach, that sporting flies
  Between the humble Earth and lofty skyes,
  Manag'd to rise and fall with little Pains,

Like the uncertain Stock that turns our Brains.
Liquors, the best, are also vended here,
From Heav'nly Punch to Halsey's Noble Beer,
By gen'rous Whitehead, who deserves the Bays
From all the Sons of Malt that Merit praise;
Therefore, if any will prove the Poet just,
Thither repair and you will surely find
Your entertainment good and Landlord kind."

In a map of London of the middle of the eighteenth century Moorfields is shown divided up into three sectors, Upper, Middle, and Lower. The site of the Upper Moorfields is now marked by Finsbury Square, and that of Lower Moorfields by Finsbury Circus; Middle Moorfields lay between the two.

It was at the north-east corner of Lower Moorfields that the Infirmary was erected. No paved roads led up to it, only tracks: one of these to the north, then called Broker Row, became Eldon Street, another leading out of London Wall to Broker Row became Blomfield Street. It was in the angle between these two streets that the Infirmary was situated. The site now occupied by Broad Street Station, directly opposite the Infirmary, was then an open space.

On the laying of the foundation-stone of the new building its name was changed, for the third time, to that of " The London Ophthalmic Infirmary "; and this was yet again altered in 1837, under circumstances that will be mentioned later, to that which it now bears, " The Royal London Ophthalmic Hospital." The name, however, by which it is most generally known is " The Moorfields Eye Hospital," though it has never been officially so designated.

It was not the first " Moorfields Hospital "; if a patient had said that he had been an inmate of " The Moorfields Hospital " in the eighteenth century he would have been regarded as an escaped lunatic. " The Bethlehem Royal Hospital " for lunatics was built on the south side of Lower Moorfields in 1675; it was a substantial building accommodating 150 patients, and remained in existence

PLATE VI.

THE LONDON OPHTHALMIC INFIRMARY AS FIRST ERECTED AT MOORFIELDS IN 1822.

From an engraving by R. Acon, after a drawing by Tho. H. Shepherd.

until 1815, when it was removed to Lambeth. To go and see the lunatics at Moorfields was for over 200 years one of the sights of London, the public being admitted to view the poor wretches on the payment of a small charge. It is stated that as much as £400 a year was received towards the upkeep of the Institution in this way; the chains with which the patients were secured and the other sufferings to which they were subjected is, however, not part of this history.

The architect of the Ophthalmic Infirmary, Robert Smirke, R.A., who was knighted in 1832, has left his mark deeply impressed on London; to him we owe, amongst other important London buildings, the British Museum, Covent Garden Theatre, the East Wing of Somerset House, the College of Physicians, and the Carlton and other Clubs. The Infirmary in its original state was a plain, unpretentious, but not unpleasing structure; in later years, whatever merits its external appearances originally possessed were destroyed by the addition of a new wing on one side and an upper storey. It originally consisted of three floors, a flight of stone steps leading up to the entrance hall in the centre of the ground floor. The out-patient consulting room was on the right of the entrance hall, and a room was specially set apart for Dr. Farre's use on the left. In the basement, besides the kitchen, etc., there were the porters' and maids' rooms, and the one bathroom and wash-house. On the first floor, in the centre, was the operating theatre, on the right a committee room, and on the left a room designated as the library, but not used as such for some years. The apothecary and the nurse-housekeeper also had their apartments on this floor, the second floor being devoted to wards for the patients.

The in-patients in the house in Charterhouse Square were restricted to operation cases, and cases of purulent ophthalmia; with increased accommodation in the new building no such restrictions were made, and a nurse was engaged to assist the nurse-housekeeper. To relieve the apothecary of some of his duties, a professional cupper was appointed to attend three days a week, and a room was set apart for him in the basement in which to carry on his sanguinary proceedings.

Smirke, the architect, advised the Committee of the Infirmary, and as afterwards turned out most wisely, to secure the vacant land in its immediate vicinity with a view to possible future extensions. The ground immediately behind the Infirmary, having a frontage of 36 feet to the north and a depth of 69 feet, had already been disposed of by the City to a Mr. Turner, who consented to part with his purchase for £15 per annum, or at twenty years' purchase, £300, for which latter it was ultimately secured.

When the building of the new Infirmary was completed, work commenced there without any ceremonial opening procedure. The first committee meeting held in it was on October 2nd, 1822, and it must have been opened for the reception of patients the same month.

On November 12th, 1822, Dr. Farre delivered to the pupils an introductory lecture in which he announced the arrangement of the following courses of instruction:

Lectures on Morbid Anatomy illustrative of the Practice of Physic in general, as well as Ophthalmic Medicine in particular. To be given occasionally and separately announced. By Dr. J. R. Farre, Physician to the Infirmary.

Lectures of the Anatomy, Physiology, and Diseases of the Eye. First Course on Tuesdays, Thursdays, and Saturdays at half-past 5 o'clock. Second and subsequent courses on Tuesdays and Saturdays at the same hour. By Mr. William Lawrence, F.R.S., Senior Surgeon to the Infirmary. ---

Clinical Lectures, on select cases of Ophthalmic Diseases occurring in the In- or Out-Patients of the Infirmary. To be given on days and at hours adapted to the convenience of the pupils. By Mr. F. Tyrrell, Junior Surgeon of the Infirmary.

Lectures in Optics. To be given on Thursdays at 7 o'clock in the evening.
By the Rev. T. Gill, M.A., Hon. Chaplain to the Infirmary.

———————

Dr. Farre concluded his announcement of these lectures with the following remarks:

" There remains one subject of great interest—The Chemistry of Light—to which I have invited the attention of Mr. Battley, not because he was the oldest and most faithful friend of Mr. Saunders, but because he has actually worked for a long time at that part of the subject which respects the vegetable kingdom, and his labour has deservedly attracted the attention of the College of Physicians. I think that the profession is much obliged to him, and I shall do everything in my power to promote his very interesting enquiries respecting the composition and decomposition of those more important vegetable substances which form a part of the Materia Medica. His success in the decomposition of opium, and in the discovering the *Liquor Opii Sedativus*, one of the most valuable preparations of opium, whether externally applied for the mitigation of extreme suffering, as in the cancerous fungi of the eye and other parts of the body, or internally administered for the cure of various irritative diseases, and his beautiful preservation of the natural green pigment and medical virtues of other preparations of the narcotic tribe, as *Digitalis Conium*, and the like, induced me, in July last, to invite him to communicate his thoughts on those subjects to the class of the Infirmary, and, in a letter received only this day, he has led me to hope that he will indulge my wishes in the spring of the ensuing year."

To what extent this ambitious programme of instructions was carried out is uncertain. Of Dr. Farre's teaching but few records remain; with regard to it, Lawrence said in the introductory chapter of his treatise:

" Dr. Farre set the example at the Infirmary, of applying the general principles of pathology and therapeutics to the elucidation and treatment of ophthalmic diseases. In the clinical illustration of cases, the exposition of curative indications and simplicity of treatment, he could not be surpassed.

All who have had the advantage of his instructions will remember them with gratitude and respect, and will regret that he has not communicated to the public, through the Press, the interesting results of his long practice, his close observation and mature reflection."

The report of one of his lectures at the Infirmary in the *Lancet* gives anything but a good impression of him as a teacher; it is a long rambling discourse, professedly on the cardiac system, with but scant reference to eye disease, and set out with scriptural quotations and protests against materialism. We learn, however, from it that he had previously delivered a course of lectures on the gastric system as applicable to ophthalmic medicine.

Lawrence's lectures were reported as they were delivered in the *Lancet* in 1825–26, and subsequently formed the basis of his treatise. The Rev. T. Gill resigned his appointment as Chaplain to the Infirmary in February, 1823, owing to some disrespectful behaviour to him on the part of the housekeeper, for which she was duly reprimanded. So he could only have given one course of instruction on optics; there is no record of any of his successors taking on a similar duty.

A room in the basement, which it had been suggested to Battley might be used by him as a laboratory and museum, was not found suitable for that purpose, and the courses of instruction which it was suggested that he might give in Materia Medica seem to have been left in abeyance until the establishment of what was termed " The Saunderian Institution."

Besides the unoccupied land behind the Infirmary, already referred to, there was another piece to the south of it, lying between it and the Roman Catholic Chapel. The leasehold of this was offered to, and secured by, Dr. Farre, who subsequently transferred it to the Infirmary. Part of the agreement permitted the previous owner of the lease to erect a stable for his own use on about two-thirds of the site, for which he was to pay only a peppercorn rent. On the remaining one-third, Dr. Farre obtained permission to erect, at the expense of the Saunderian Fund, which had been established by him, a building to be called " The Saunderian Institution." The purpose of this Institution was the cultivation of minute anatomy, especially of the eye, and a general analysis of the Materia Medica to increase the remedial agents of the Hospital, as well as benefit the profession. The management of the Institution was to remain entirely in the hands of Dr. Farre during his life.

" The Saunderian Fund " was one specially established for the erection of a monument to John Cunningham Saunders; to it Dr. Farre himself contributed £120, and to it also were added the proceeds of the sale of the second edition of Saunders' book edited by Dr. Farre. Out of the fund a bust of the late J. C. Saunders was constructed, which now stands in the entrance hall of the present Hospital; the remainder of it seems to have been devoted to this Institution.

In the year 1827, the Laboratory of the Institution was opened by Mr. Battley for the analysis of the vegetable substances of the Materia Medica, with a view to the improvement of Pharmacy, by showing wherein the efficient powers of these substances reside and by what means the most useful preparations of them may be obtained. It appears that he held large classes of students there, more than 2,000 from various Medical Schools, British and foreign, having attended for instruction.

Dr. Farre, in an Introductory Lecture entitled " Apology for British Anatomy," at the opening of the pathological department of the Institute, or Academy, as he sometimes described it, pointed out that the objects which it had in view were: the study of the anatomy of structure; the performance of post-mortem examinations; the study of minute morbid anatomy; the publication of a journal; the publication of separate essays; the cultivation of the Fine Arts of drawing and modelling as connected with minute practical and morbid anatomy.

John Dalrymple, who afterwards became a surgeon to the Ophthalmic Infirmary, was appointed demonstrator and secretary to the Academy.

In connection with the announcement of Lawrence's resignation of his post of surgeon to the Ophthalmic Infirmary in 1826, there commenced a series of editorial articles in the *Lancet*, attacking members of the Committee of Management and imputing to them the most base and degrading motives.

The *Lancet* had been founded in 1823 by Thomas Wakley, and at first, as his biographer says, " Some men read it, some men laughed at it, and some men wondered at it, but nobody much marked it, for its views were not sufficiently condensed and its objects not definitely defined."

In 1825 Tyrrell summoned Wakley for libel, claiming £2,000 damages, in that the *Lancet* had accused Tyrrell of plagiarism in connection with his publication of Astley Cooper's Surgical Lectures. Though the jury gave their verdict in Tyrrell's favour, they only assessed his damages at £50.

Gradually after this trial the policy of the *Lancet* became directed to three main objects:

(1) The maintenance of a right to publish, for the benefit of the profession at large, the sayings and doings of members of the Hospital Staffs, with or without their permission.

(2) A fight against nepotism in the matter of staff appointments at the Hospitals.

(3) An exposure of, what Wakley delighted in calling, a " Hole in the Corner Policy " by members of Hospital Staffs—*i.e.*, the employment of secretive methods in their practice.

In the affairs of the Ophthalmic Infirmary Wakley found a suitable field for attack in these three directions, and, though his objects may have been excellent, his mode of conducting his campaign was inconsiderately bitter and personal.

For the unauthorised publication in his Journal of the notes of cases at St. Thomas's Hospital, Wakley had been expelled from that Institution, where he had studied as a student, the letter of expulsion being signed by the three surgeons, Travers, Tyrrell, and Green.

Lawrence, who was at that time a prominent medical reformer, and for whom Wakley evidently had a great admiration, welcomed the publication of his lectures, delivered at the Ophthalmic Infirmary, in the *Lancet*.

Tyrrell, who had been prominent in the fight against Wakley at St. Thomas's and who had also taken legal proceedings against him, resented having his demonstrations at the Ophthalmic Infirmary reported in the Journal. On this matter there may very likely have been some disagreement between the two surgeons of the Infirmary. There is no note in the minute book of the Committee of any discussion on the matter having taken place, or of any bye-law being passed to the effect that " no pupil should be allowed in future to take notes of cases." Wakley, therefore, seems to have been wrong in attributing Lawrence's resignation of his post on the staff of the Infirmary to his disgust with the Committee for having passed such a bye-law. When the *Lancet's* first attacks on Dr. Farre and Mr. Battley were brought to the notice of the Committee, Lawrence protested emphatically that neither directly nor indirectly had he been in any way concerned in them. The real reason of his resignation probably was that he had become connected with the newly constituted Aldersgate Street School of Medicine, where he delivered a course of lectures on Surgery.

As has been mentioned, the idea of establishing a special institution for treating diseases of the eye was originally suggested to Saunders by Sir Astley Cooper, who always took a fatherly interest in it. It was, therefore, inevitable that, to commence with, it should be mainly staffed by his disciples and followers. Saunders had been his house pupil and demonstrator; Travers and Tyrrell were both his articled pupils, the latter having also married his niece.

Farre and Battley had both studied under him. In making his charge of nepotism, Wakley complained chiefly of the rule which made it obligatory that a candidate for the post of surgeon should have served an apprenticeship at one of the Hospitals of the Metropolis. He pointed out that for these apprenticeships to the London Hospital surgeons a premium of as much as £1,000 was sometimes demanded and received, and that those for whom these large sums were paid thereby obtained an unfair advantage when competing for staff appointments likely to lead to renown and emoluments.

He also commented on a rumour that a post of assistant-physician to the Infirmary was about to be created, to which Dr. Frederick Farre, Dr. J. R. Farre's son, was to be appointed. This, as we shall see, did ultimately take place, but not until ten years later and after the post had been duly advertised, Dr. Frederick Farre being the only applicant.

The Infirmary's announcement of Saunders' operation for cataract in infancy, before he had made known to the profession his method of procedure, afforded Wakley an excellent illustration of secret surgery, or " Hole in the Corner methods " as he termed them. He eagerly made the most of it, raking up what he considered the misdeeds of Saunders, who had been dead seventeen years, and whom he had never known personally. He reprinted much of Gibson's article on operations for congenital cataract from the *Edinburgh Medical and Surgical Journal*, to show that the publication of his procedure actually preceded Farre's publication of Saunders' posthumous work by two months. He even accused Dr. Farre of wilful delay in the matter, a delay which was entirely due to the difficulties which arose in connection with the copyright.

The Committee of the Infirmary took legal advice in connection with these defamatory articles, but contented itself with the insertion of the following letter in *The Times* and other leading papers:

" London Ophthalmic Infirmary, Moorfields.

" At a meeting of the Committee, 6th November, 1826, Ralph Price, Esq., in the Chair, five numbers of a weekly publication, called the *Lancet*, dated the 7th, 14th, 21st and 28th October last, and 4th instant, and *The Times* newspaper of the 28th October, were laid before the Meeting; the former containing false statements and offensive reflections upon the Members of this Committee in their official capacities, but in a particular manner calculated to insult the memory of the late Mr. Saunders, and wound the feelings of Dr. Farre and Mr. Battley; and the latter echoing similar calumnies in the form of a letter, directed ' to the Editor of *The Times* ' and signed ' A Governor '; when it was resolved : That the freedom of the Press has been violated, by becoming, in the instances referred to, an instrument of gross malignity and abuse, and of the foulest injustice towards two of the earliest and most tried supporters of the Charity; that this Meeting experiences the greatest satisfaction in again bearing testimony to the high value of Dr. Farre's and Mr. Battley's undeviating and disinterested exertions during a period of twenty-two years, which, in conjunction with their liberal pecuniary subscriptions, have largely contributed to the rise and establishment of this Institution.

" That this Resolution, signed by the Chairman, be inserted in four of the Morning and two of the Evening Papers.
" Ralph Price, *Chairman*."

On the retirement of Lawrence from the post of surgeon to the Infirmary, John Scott, who had served his apprenticeship at the London Hospital with Sir William Blizard, was appointed as Tyrrell's colleague.

Lawrence, as has been shown in the previous chapter, was what may be described as " a whole hogger," so far as withdrawal of blood was concerned for the relief of inflammation in the eye. Tyrrell, though he employed it in many cases, was evidently doubtful as to its general utility; thus he writes in his textbook:

" It is a great mistake to suppose that it is necessary to take away large quantities of blood; or to bleed to such an extent as to occasion faintness, in order to check severe local disease: I am confident that more harm than good results from such practice."

He advocated the importance of promoting and maintaining power in the circulation, the principal means on which he relied being " diet, stimuli, and tonics, which are materially aided by quietude, proper clothing, and pure air."

In the preparation for extraction of cataract, to prevent subsequent inflammation, especially in the robust and plethoric, Lawrence practised depletion, taking blood freely and repeatedly by venesection before operation. Gradually this preliminary measure seems to have been less and less resorted to, and, in a small monograph on *Cataract and its Treatment*, published by Scott in 1843, he writes:

" Of the last fifty cases of extraction, taken in succession, which I have performed at the Ophthalmic Hospital, where an accurate record of the treatment is kept, I have not had occasion to draw blood from the arm in a single instance, either before or after the operation."

An anonymous writer has recorded his personal recollections of Tyrrell thus:

" His appearance was prepossessing, his manner to his patients kind and reassuring, and his calmness was conspicuous in circumstances of difficulty. It is a singular fact that, when first attached to Moorfields, his ill success as an operator was so great that he was suspended from performing the major operations for a year; yet by steady perseverance he acquired a dexterity with either hand that could not be surpassed. In extraction of cataract his neatness was remarkable, and we well remember an instance of his coolness. The point of the section knife broke off, and dropped into the anterior chamber. Mr. Tyrrell withdrew the knife, and without the least expression of impatience, asked for the blunt-pointed knife, with which he enlarged the section. He then removed the bit of steel and proceeded to extract the lens with such perfect *sang froid* that no one

PLATE VII.

FREDERICK TYRRELL.

[To face p. 62

who had not seen the breaking of the knife would have known that anything untoward had occurred.

" Mr. Tyrrell's great success depended fully as much on his judicious after-treatment as on his manual dexterity; and his secret lay in not exhausting the systems of his patients unnecessarily, but keeping the balance of power precisely at healing point.

" On a hot day in May, 1843, whilst an active competition for a house was going on at the Auction Mart, an alarm was raised that a gentleman had fainted. He was carried out. Alas ! it was Frederick Tyrrell, who had attended the sale for the purpose of purchasing the very lot then under competition, which, indeed, was the house he occupied. His heart was diseased and thus he died !"

In 1840 he published a book in two volumes entitled *A Practical Work on the Diseases of the Eye and their Treatment, Medically, Topically, and by Operation.* It was dedicated to his ophthalmic pupils, and contained the outcome of the extensive experience which he had gained at the Infirmary. His memory has, however, become enshrined in the annals of ophthalmology, not so much by his writings, as by a blunt hook which he introduced for the operation of making an artificial pupil, which is still known as " Tyrrell's hook," and without which no ophthalmic armamentarium is complete.

It is interesting here to note how far more frequent operations to produce an artificial pupil were one hundred years ago than they are now. In all the early treatises on eye disease much space was devoted to the discussion of the various methods of producing such artificial openings for the restoration of sight. The only inference is that occlusion of the natural pupil by inflammatory membranes was then of more frequent occurrence, and that the improved methods of treating inflammatory eye affections, and the more successful operative procedures for cataract, have reduced the number of such occlusions.

In 1828 a body of ladies interested in the Charity carried

out a most successful sale of useful and ornamental work on its behalf. The President of the Infirmary, Mr. William Mellish, obtained for the sale the patronage of the Lord and Lady Mayoress, and permission to hold it in the Egyptian Hall at the Mansion House. The sale commenced on April 30th, and lasted three days; stalls were presided over by thirteen ladies, and the sum of £2,309 9s. 6d. was realised.

On the announcement of this result at a General Meeting of Governors a long and flowery resolution of thanks was passed to all concerned, of which the opening sentence will suffice as an example of the rest:

" That this unprecedented success of the plan conceived with so much benevolence and executed with so much zeal and ability by the ladies who have honoured the Institution with their patronage on this occasion, whilst it reflects the highest honour on the ingenuity, industry and charity, which combined to produce so beneficial a result, is eminently conducive to the best interests of the Infirmary and highly gratifying to its Governors and friends."

In 1830 Tyrrell, who had been carrying on the duties of surgeon to the Institution for twelve years, became desirous of receiving some aid, and applied to the Committee for the appointment of an assistant-surgeon; this was agreed to, and after the post had been advertised two applicants came forward, Gilbert Mackmurdo and John Dalrymple. In the ballot which ensued 591 Governors voted, Mackmurdo, who had served his apprenticeship under Travers at St. Thomas's Hospital, obtaining a majority of 143.

Two years later it was found desirable to open the Infirmary for out-patients on four days a week instead of three, as had up to then been the custom, and also to make the hours of attendance from 8 a.m. until 10 a.m. instead of from 12 noon to 2 p.m. A second assistant-surgeon was then appointed to act with John Scott, and John Dalrymple, who was the only applicant, was elected.

John Scott, shortly after his appointment as surgeon to

PLATE VIII.

JOHN SCOTT.

From an engraving, after a picture by H. Howard, R.A.

[To face p. 65

the Infirmary, was appointed assistant-surgeon to the London Hospital, becoming full surgeon there in 1831. He continued his work at the Ophthalmic Infirmary until shortly before his death, which occurred after a prolonged illness in 1846.

His name is best remembered in General Surgery in connection with his treatment of joints and chronic ulcers of the leg. "Scott's dressing" and "Scott's ointment" are still well known, the latter being a camphorated mercurial ointment. He was the first surgeon in England to remove the upper jaw, and was renowned for his skill in bandaging. His only published contribution to ophthalmology was a small monograph on *Cataract and its Treatment*, in which he described a new method of making the section of the cornea in the operation of extraction. It had previously been the custom to use a wedge-shaped knife for this purpose, which was made to cut by thrusting it through the anterior chamber of the eye; the force necessary to do so tended to rotate the eyeball in an objectionable manner. Scott devised a knife, shaped like a sickle, with which he was able to transfix the cornea and then cut upwards. Though his knife has fallen completely out of use, the general principle of first transfixing and then cutting out is now almost universally employed. The writer of his obituary notice, his junior colleague at the London Hospital, Walter Rivington, describes him as "an honest but very irritable man," and one who had no sympathy with humanity.

Another writer who knew him says:

"A colleague of Frederick Tyrrell's at Moorfields was John Scott, who presented as great a contrast to the former as could well be imagined. Impatient and irritable in manner, he could not bear anything to go wrong; no man lost vitreous humour more frequently during extraction, at which he was invariably annoyed, ascribing it, however, to 'fluidity' of that body."

A great loss to the Infirmary in 1835 was occasioned by the death of its secretary, Matthew Heathfield, who had served it in that capacity with marked assiduity and enthusiasm for fifteen years. His successor only held the office for a few months before he was obliged to give it up on account of ill-health. In April, 1835, Francis William Bircham was appointed secretary at a salary of £52 10s. annually. It is noteworthy that the firm of solicitors to which he belonged, Messrs. Bircham, Dalrymple and Drake, now Messrs. Bircham and Co., of 46, Parliament Street, S.W. 1, still act as honorary solicitors to the Hospital.

CHAPTER V

THE ROYAL LONDON OPHTHALMIC HOSPITAL

His Royal Highness the Duke of York, the Infirmary's first Patron, died in 1827.

At the three days' sale at the Mansion House in 1828 the Duchess of Kent was one of the Lady Patronesses. In 1836 the Rev. Dr. Blomberg, a member of the General Committee of the Infirmary, stated that he had reasons to hope that an application to their Royal Highnesses the Duchess of Kent and the Princess Victoria to become Patronesses of the Institution would be likely to meet with success. A letter was then drawn up, addressed to the Rev. Dr. Blomberg, and signed by the President, with a statement of the following claims by the Institution to so high a distinction: That the grand total of patients admitted since its establishment to the end of 1835 (a period of about thirty years) was 116,890, during which time 1,070 cases of cataract or closed pupil (including 136 born blind) had had their sight restored. That the annual number of patients admitted of late years had varied from 5,000 to 5,500. That 74 capital operations were performed in 1834, 69 of which were successful, and of 78 performed in 1835 four only failed to produce the desired effect. That no less than 1,320 physicians and surgeons had been pupils at the Infirmary, and were now dispensing its benefits in various parts of the globe. That it was the parent institution of the numerous hospitals since established throughout the kingdom for the same benevolent purpose.

It was requested that the Rev. Dr. Blomberg would bring these facts before the notice of the Duchess of Kent and her illustrious daughter, the Heiress-Presumptive to

67

the Throne, requesting their gracious permission to place the Institution under their august patronage.

In response to this petition the following letters were received:

"KENSINGTON PALACE,
"12th March, 1836.

"MY DEAR SIR,
    "By the accompanying letter which you will be so good as to forward you will see that the Duchess of Kent has lent her aid and that of the Princess Victoria to the excellent charity whose cause was so ably advocated in Mr. Mellish's letter.

"Her Royal Highness is very happy to find an occasion to meet a wish of yours.

"Believe me always, my dear Sir,
"Yours very faithfully,
"JOHN CONROY.

"THE REV. DR. BLOMBERG."

"KENSINGTON PALACE,
"12th March, 1836.

"SIR,
    "I have the honour to lay before the Duchess of Kent your letter of yesterday's date, and Her Royal Highness begs you will assure the Committee of the London Ophthalmic Infirmary, Moorfields, that it will be very gratifying to her to allow her name and that of Her Royal Highness the Princess Victoria to be placed as Patronesses of so benevolent an Institution.

"I have the honour to be, Sir,
"Your most obedient servant,
"JOHN CONROY.

"WM. MELLISH, ESQ.,
"112, BISHOPSGATE STREET WITHOUT."

As the outcome of the Royal Patronage, it was agreed at a General Meeting of Governors, on April 20th, 1836, that the name of the Institution should be changed to "The Royal London Ophthalmic Hospital, Moorfields."

In 1837, on Queen Victoria's accession to the Throne, the Chairman of the Committee of the Hospital applied to Lord John Russell, the Secretary of State for the Home Department, to ascertain Her Majesty's pleasure as to continuing Patroness of the Hospital, and received from him the following reply:

"WHITEHALL,
"*August 29th,* 1837.
" SIR,
"I have the honour to lay before the Queen the petition of the Committee of Management of the Royal Ophthalmic Hospital.

"And I have the satisfaction to inform you that Her Majesty has been graciously pleased to be the Patroness of that Hospital.

"I have the honour to be, Sir,
"Your obedient servant,
"J. RUSSELL.
" THE REV. J. RUSSELL, D.D., etc.,
"RECTORY HOUSE,
"DEVONSHIRE SQUARE."

The Patronage of the Queen, thus commenced, continued throughout the whole of her long reign.

In 1838 William Mellish, who had been President of the Hospital for twenty years, died, and the Committee placed on record their gratitude and respect for the uninterrupted paternal care and attention he had shown to the interests of the Institution during his time of office. He was what may be described as a real live President, having been always ready to take the Chair at the annual meetings of Governors and at the anniversary dinners. He was succeeded in the office of President by Earl Fitzwilliam, who resided mainly in the country, and but seldom visited the Hospital, so that the control of its affairs fell largely into the hands of the Chairman of the General Committee, who was at that time the Rev. J. Russell, D.D.

It was obvious at the foundation of a special institution devoted to eye diseases that the treatment would be mainly surgical, but the importance of the medical side of ophthalmology was recognised by the appointment of a physician. With the expansion of the work of the Institution during the first thirty years of its existence the number of surgeons on the staff had to be increased from one to four. During all that time Dr. J. R. Farre acted alone as consulting physician, having referred to him for his advice and aid cases requiring medical treatment. In 1836, when he had reached the age of sixty-one, a special Committee, of which he was not a member, decided that it was desirable to appoint an assistant-physician; the post was advertised in the daily journals, and Dr. Frederick John Farre, assistant-physician at St. Bartholomew's Hospital, son of Dr. J. R. Farre, was appointed, he being the only candidate. It was then arranged that the Hospital should be opened for out-patients, to be seen by the assistant-physician, on Wednesday mornings at eight o'clock, and that notices to that effect should be advertised.

In turning over the leaves of the minute books recording the doings of the various Committees, it is remarkable to find how much time and attention Dr. J. R. Farre devoted to the management and administration of the Infirmary during its first thirty years. Travers aptly described him as " the foster-father of the London Ophthalmic Infirmary." He has also aptly been described as " the father of Ophthalmic Medicine." He was most regular in his attendance, and when a petition, a report, or any letter of importance had to be composed, his assistance was always sought for. Though his style now seems florid and verbose, it met the requirements of the time, and generally effected the purpose for which it was intended.

With remarkable foresight he endeavoured to establish, with varying degrees of success, many of the developments which have in later years become some of the most prominent features of the Hospital's work. Thus the Saunderian Institute, one of the purposes of which was the investigation of the minute anatomy of the eye, foreshadowed the Pathological Laboratory and Museum which were established later.

In 1828 Dr. Farre started the publication of a Journal, of which, however, only one number appeared, but in a way it may be considered the precursor of the Royal London Ophthalmic Hospital Reports, which commenced in 1857. Farre's Journal contained a most remarkable mixture of subjects, and serves to show him as a man of wide and varied interests.

It was entitled, *Journal of Morbid Anatomy, Ophthalmic Medicine and Pharmaceutical Analysis, with Medico-Botanical Transactions communicated by the Medico-Botanical Society*.

It contained reports from the Calcutta and Madras Eye Infirmaries; notes on cases and pathological examinations of rupture of the heart, angina pectoris, aneurysm, etc., by various observers; a paper by Richard Battley on experiments on Chinchona; the Transactions of the Medico-Botanical Society; observations on the climate of the Azores, of Hastings, and Penzance; a paper by John Dalrymple, " On the Muscularity of the Iris," which, Dr. Farre said, in some introductory remarks, met the principal object for which his Academy was instituted—

" the inquiry having been physiologically conducted and pathologically directed, assumed the very spirit which he most desired to encourage amongst the many British candidates for anatomical character."

It was announced that:

" Parts of the Journal will be published at fixed periods of Midsummer and Christmas, and also intervening parts, as opportunity may admit, for the completion of each volume, if the Editor's health should, by God's permission, enable him to separate from the hours of his repose a portion of time adequate to the service announced in this notice to contributors."

These good intentions were, however, not realised, no further number of the Journal being issued.

The Library, for which a special room had been set apart in the new building, was started by Dr. J. R. Farre's presentation of eighteen volumes of the Philosophical Transactions and various works on optics. These formed a nucleus around which has been built up one of the most extensive and valuable collections of books dealing with ophthalmology, a collection which has proved of inestimable service for purposes of reference and research to several successive generations of workers at the Hospital.

In 1837 Dr. J. R. Farre advised the Committee that it was desirable that a Pharmacopœia should be constructed for the use of the Hospital; in its compilation Dr. Frederick Farre, who was lecturer on Botany at St. Bartholomew's Hospital, and later lecturer there on Materia Medica, rendered valuable assistance.

Dr. Farre, senior, seems to have been a man who inspired the warmest regard and affection in all who became associated with him; in 1838 a full-length portrait of him was presented to the Hospital by some of his friends with the accompanying letter:

" LONDON, 18th August, 1838.
" 34, MONTAGU SQUARE.
" GENTLEMEN,
" I have the honour on behalf of my brothers and myself to present to the Royal London Ophthalmic Hospital, of which he has so long been a liberal patron and zealous benefactor, a portrait of our esteemed friend Dr. John Richard Farre, painted by T. Phillips, R.A.

" To those who appreciate the character and services of the worthy original we feel assured that we need only offer in order to obtain for it a welcome reception.
" I am, Gentlemen,
" Your most obedient servant,
" J. ROACH BOVELL.
" THE PRESIDENT, VICE-PRESIDENTS,
TREASURER AND COMMITTEE OF THE R.L.O.H."

On receiving it the Committee passed the following resolution:

PLATE IX.

DR. JOHN RICHARD FARRE.
From an engraving by Frank Bromley, after a picture by Thomas Phillips, R.A.

[To face p. 73

"That recognising in Dr. Farre not only one of the Founders of the Institution but a munificent contributor to its funds, and the able physician by whom the science communicated and dispensed within its walls has been effectively upheld and enlarged, the Committee accepts the testimonial of private esteem and affection with peculiar pleasure as the means of publicly manifesting, and of transmitting to posterity, the high claims of public respect and gratitude for that highly distinguished public benefactor."

Thomas Phillips, R.A., painted the portraits of most of the celebrated literary and scientific men of his time; that of Dr. Farre must certainly have been one of his largest works of this description. It now occupies a dominating position in the Board Room of the Hospital, and shows Dr. Farre clothed in stockings and knee-breeches, with a buff-coloured waistcoat, stock, and blue coat with brass buttons. He is represented seated at a table with the drawing of a malformed heart in one hand, and a portfolio beside him, evidently containing his valuable collection of drawings of pathological specimens, which was afterwards presented to St. Bartholomew's Hospital Museum.

Dr. Farre was a religiously devout man, and most appropriately there is conspicuously shown amongst the books on his table a copy of the Holy Bible. He continued to serve the Hospital in the capacity of consulting physician until 1843, but lived on until 1862, when he died in his eighty-eighth year, having outlived all those who had been associated with him in the Hospital's foundation.

His son, Dr. Frederick J. Farre, was educated at Charterhouse School, and was the captain of it during Thackeray's first year there. Thackeray afterwards introduced him in *The Adventures of Philip* as Sampson Major, the cock of the whole school.

Mackmurdo and Dalrymple's duties as assistant-surgeons consisted mainly in the treatment of the out-patients. After having been so employed for several years, they not unnaturally aspired to gaining skill and experience in the performance of the major operations of ophthalmic surgery on the in-patients. With such aspirations several members of the Committee of Management were in sympathy, and much discussion took place as to some alteration in the rules which would permit of them acting as full surgeons. Tyrrell and Scott, however, were opposed to any proposal which was likely to lead to a curtailment of their privileges as senior officers.

The following return was drawn up and laid before the Committee to show how the work of the Institution was distributed amongst the different members of the medical staff in the year 1842.

Out-patients:

Dr. F. Farre	.. ..	607 (one day a week)
Mr. Tyrrell	.. ..	1,090
Mr. Scott	.. ..	1,037 (two days a week)
Mr. Mackmurdo	..	1,274
Mr. Dalrymple ..	..	1,714

Operations performed:

	Extraction of Cataract.	Needling of Cataract.	Artificial Pupil.
Mr. Tyrrell ..	42	20	7
Mr. Scott ..	29	9	7
Mr. Mackmurdo	0	4	0
Mr. Dalrymple	0	5	0

The matter was brought to a head by the death of Tyrrell in June, 1843. By that time Mackmurdo had served the Hospital as assistant-surgeon for a period of thirteen years, and Dalrymple for eleven years.

After due notice had been given it was then agreed, at a special General Meeting of the Governors, that the laws regarding the appointment of the medical officers should be suspended, and that Mr. Mackmurdo and Mr. Dalrymple should forthwith be appointed surgeons to the Hospital; also that two new assistant-surgeons should be elected.

Mr. John Scott strongly protested against such an increase in the surgical staff, pointing out, quite correctly, that such an increase was out of proportion to the increase in the number of patients.

Shortly afterwards Dr. Frederick J. Farre was likewise promoted from assistant-physician to physician to the Hospital, his father, Dr. J. R. Farre, being described as consulting physician, the capacity in which he claimed to have always served as a member of the staff.

The candidates for the two posts of assistant-surgeon were:

Mr. James Dixon, who had been articled as apprentice to Tyrrell, and who was demonstrator of anatomy at St. Thomas's Hospital.

Mr. George Critchett, who had been articled to Scott, and who was demonstrator of anatomy at the London Hospital.

Mr. William Bowman, who had served his apprenticeship at the Birmingham Hospital, and who was demonstrator of anatomy at King's College Hospital.

The latter withdrew his candidature in favour of the two former when he found that they had been already working at the Hospital, but at the same time intimated his intention of applying again when a further vacancy arose. This occurred in 1846, due to Scott's retirement from ill-health, and Bowman was then elected assistant-surgeon unopposed.

Dr. J. R. Farre was, as already shown, a man of ideas as well as of affairs; the time, however, occupied by the latter precluded his putting many of the former into practice. He was, therefore, exceedingly fortunate in finding in John Dalrymple a most energetic and capable disciple.

John Dalrymple, who was related to the Stair family, was born in 1803. His father, William Dalrymple, who had studied under Astley Cooper, was surgeon to the Norfolk and Norwich Hospital. He was a liberal-minded man as well as a skilful surgeon, and attracted considerable attention in 1813 by repeating successfully Travers' operation of tying the common carotid artery in a case of " aneurism by anastomosis " of the orbit. He had also devoted some attention to ocular pathology, and had made a valuable collection of anatomical and pathological preparations, which he presented to the Norfolk and Norwich Hospital.

John seems to have served his apprenticeship under his father, and to have acquired from him a liking for both pathology and ophthalmology. He studied for a time at Edinburgh University, and came to London, where he qualified as M.R.C.S. in 1827.

His association with Dr. Farre and with the Moorfields Hospital then commenced, with his appointment already mentioned, as demonstrator and secretary to the newly opened Saunderian Institution, where he carried out anatomical and pathological investigations. In 1834, as the outcome of his work at the Institute, he published a treatise on the *Anatomy of the Human Eye*, which he dedicated to Dr. J. R. Farre, Frederick Tyrrell, and John Scott, his colleagues at the Infirmary, to which he had been appointed assistant-surgeon the previous year. This book, besides containing a description of his own dissections, gives an excellent review of the work of previous investigators, and is illustrated by five engraved plates from his own anatomical drawings. · Dalrymple's investigations were not restricted to ophthalmology; between the years 1840 and 1849 he contributed several papers to the Medico-Chirurgical Society's Transactions relating to general pathology, and also wrote articles dealing with Natural History.

Tyrrell's unexpected decease, and later Scott's retirement, left Dalrymple in a leading position in ophthalmology, and his reputation and practice rapidly increased. In 1847 he found the state of his health to be such as to render it impossible for him to keep up his attendance at the Hospital during the winter months. As he was the only surgeon in attendance on Wednesdays and Saturdays, whereas on the other days of the week both a surgeon and an assistant-surgeon were on duty, the Governors agreed to appoint a third assistant-surgeon, and thereby relieve Dalrymple of his duties during the winter. Alfred Poland, who had served his apprenticeship under Aston Key at Guy's Hospital, and who was a demonstrator of anatomy there, was elected to the post.

Dalrymple's health did not tend to improve, and in 1849 he felt compelled to resign his appointment on the active staff, and was appointed consulting surgeon. On his retirement no fresh appointment was made to the staff, Critchett being promoted to the post of surgeon in his place. In 1850 Dalrymple was elected a Fellow of the Royal Society.

For a number of years John Scott and Dalrymple had been collecting water-coloured drawings of diseases of the eye, made from patients under their care at the Hospital by the best artists. Scott, at his death, bequeathed to Dalrymple the drawings he had collected, and these, added to Dalrymple's own, amounted to several hundred. It was from a selection of them that in 1852 Dalrymple was able to produce his great Atlas of *Pathology of the Eye*. The publication of the volume was entrusted to Mr. Churchill, and every advantage that fine paper and artistic skill could afford was supplied. The Atlas consisted of thirty-six plates, some containing six figures, and others full-page illustrations, with explanatory letterpress. The original drawings were made by W. H. Kearney and Leonard, and the drawings on stone by W. Bragg. It can safely be asserted that no illustrations of eye diseases ever surpassed or even equalled those in this Atlas, both as regards artistic merits and faithfulness in the depiction of the characteristics of the conditions they represent. The cost of the production of the Atlas was nearly fifteen hundred pounds, and copies of it now are exceedingly scarce. Dalrymple only

lived a few weeks after its completion, dying in the zenith
of his fame and the full tide of prosperity. The whole
collection of drawings, from which those reproduced in the
Atlas were selected, was bequeathed by him in his will to
the library of the Royal London Ophthalmic Hospital,
where they are still preserved.

It is perhaps remarkable that, though Dalrymple did so
much for ophthalmology by his anatomical investigations
and the production of this Atlas, his name is best known
by ophthalmic surgeons at the present day in connection
with the symptom of retraction of the upper lids in " Graves'
disease " or " exophthalmic goitre," which produces the
peculiar staring look that forms one of its most characteristic
features. This symptom is spoken of in textbooks as
" Dalrymple's sign," but to his description of it Dalrymple
himself apparently attached but little importance.

John Dalrymple was one of a family of nine; two of his
brothers became medical men and practised in Norwich;
another, named Robert Francis, was a solicitor in the firm
of Bircham, Dalrymple, and Draise, and on the retirement
of Francis Bircham, his partner, from the post of secretary
to the Hospital in 1844, R. F. Dalrymple was appointed in
his place. He discharged the duties of the office most
efficiently for two years, and was then succeeded by Mr.
F. A. Curling.

Richard Battley married one of Dalrymple's sisters. John
Dalrymple died in May, 1852, and Battley in 1856. The
latter's widow, after the death of her husband, presented
to the Hospital a bust of her brother, which now stands
in the hall of the present building. In the same year, 1856,
Robert Dalrymple was elected a member of the Committee
of Management of the Hospital, and presented to it an
engraving of his brother, which still hangs in the Board
Room of the Hospital, mounted in what was described at
the time as " an elegant gilt frame." Another presentation
to the Hospital that year was a copy of Dalrymple's Atlas

PLATE X.

JOHN DALRYMPLE, F.R.S.

To face p. 78

from John Churchill, the publisher, with the following inscription on the flyleaf:

" Presented to the Royal London Ophthalmic Hospital, in honour of that sight-saving Institution, and as a memorial of the highest respect and esteem for the memory of the author, whose lamented death took place soon after the completion of his immortal work, the subscriber having enjoyed the friendship of the author, as well as being his publisher.

" (Signed) JOHN CHURCHILL.

" 6th October, 1856."

At the Annual General Meeting of the Governors of the Hospital, after the death of Richard Battley, the following resolution was passed:

" That this Meeting most gratefully acknowledge the eminent services to this Hospital of the late Mr. Richard Battley; that to his energy and perseverance are attributed more especially the establishment of the Hospital; that in its origin, when checked by impediments and surrounded by difficulties, it was fostered by his influence and exertions and, in the arduous circumstances which ensued and continued during many years, was succoured and sustained by his active zeal; and that it is especially to be recorded that he upheld the Institution by an undeviating regard to the professional appointments by which the Hospital has been distinguished from its foundation.

" That this memorial be engraved and placed in the committee room of the Hospital with the portraits of his early friends, Saunders and Farre."

Gilbert M. Mackmurdo was Dalrymple's senior; he remained a member of the active staff of the Hospital until 1856, and died at an advanced age in 1869. In his obituary notice he is said to have had a fine appearance, a fair patrimony, and to have enjoyed great City and mercantile influence; it was largely due to the latter that he obtained his early appointment to the staff at Moorfields, and that of surgeon to St. Thomas's Hospital and to Newgate Prison.

The last appointment gave him for many years a handsome salary, with a commensurate retiring allowance.

Being well provided for with this world's goods, he seems to have contented himself with the practice of the art of his profession without making contributions to its science. Early in life he was elected a Fellow of the Royal Society, but for what particular reason no record can be found. His only contribution to ophthalmic literature seems to be a short description of a case of recurrent hæmorrhage from the inferior palpebral artery. He is said to have been thoroughly popular with his pupils and with his patients of all degrees, and never, never to have made an enemy in his life, either willingly or wilfully.

In 1849 Mrs. Dodson, who had held the post of matron at the Hospital for a number of years, died, and a Committee was appointed to report on the general arrangements and accommodation of the Institution. The following extract from it serves to show what these were, after the Hospital had been in existence for half a century:

" The establishment consists of a Resident Apothecary, a Matron, one Nurse, one Housemaid, and one Cook, all of whom reside upon the premises, and a Porter or Messenger who neither sleeps nor takes his meals in the building.

" There are 23 beds for patients in five separate wards, and during the winter only from one to five are occupied, whilst during the summer, or from May to October, when the season is propitious for the various operations, the whole of the beds are occupied.

" The Committee recommends that the new Matron to be appointed should be discreet and mild in her manner, whose standing and carriage is superior to a servant, of about 40 years of age and without encumbrances, and whose duties shall be to render assistance to and alleviate the sufferings of the patients by a regular oversight of them.

" Her salary to be 30 guineas a year, with an allowance of £5 for tea and sugar."

As the fame of the Hospital extended there was a rapid increase in the patients who came to it seeking relief. The annual number of new out-patients became doubled in the course of ten years; in 1841 there were 5,643, and in 1851, 11,384.

This large increase made it necessary to provide for increased accommodation in the out-patient department. In a letter to the Committee, Dr. J. R. Farre drew attention to the early age at which the death of several of the members of the surgical staff had taken place. Saunders died at the age of thirty-six; Tyrrell at forty-nine; Scott at forty-eight; and Dalrymple at forty-nine. Farre suggested that this might to some extent be due to the tainted atmosphere of the receiving rooms for patients, and to the strain involved in having to attend to such large numbers.

A rearrangement of the rooms of the ground floor of the Hospital was then made to provide more space for those waiting to be attended to; an assistant was engaged to aid in the dispensing; and the staff was increased by the appointment of another assistant-surgeon.

The candidates for this post were Mr. H. H. Mackmurdo and Mr. T. N. Nunn; the former received 330 votes and the latter 160. The former probably, like his brother Gilbert, was able to bring considerable City and mercantile influence to assist him; he, however, only held the post for a year, and then resigned. Mr. J. C. Wordsworth, who was a descendant of a collateral branch of the poet's family, and who was an assistant-surgeon at the London Hospital, was appointed in his place.

CHAPTER VI

THE INTRODUCTION OF INHALATION ANÆS-THESIA AND OPHTHALMIC SURGERY

Ether was first employed as an anæsthetic for surgical operations in England on December 19th, 1846, when Robert Liston performed an amputation of the thigh, and the removal of a great toe-nail, on patients under its influence, at University College Hospital, Gower Street. In Edinburgh, Sir James Simpson first gave a description of his use of chloroform, at the Medico-Chirurgical Society in that city, in November, 1847.

The adoption of anæsthetics for general surgical procedures rapidly followed, but, due to the sickness by which they were often followed, their employment in ophthalmic surgery was for some time delayed. Thus, Mackenzie of Glasgow, writing in 1854, says:

" Needle operations may be performed on timid adults under the influence of chloroform. In extraction I have not ventured to use it, being afraid lest the vomiting which is apt to follow might cause rupture of the internal structures of the eye."

In a review of Haynes Walton's textbook on eye diseases in 1853, an anonymous writer says:

" We agree with Mr. Walton that it is not advisable to use chloroform in the extraction of cataract, and we would remark that a surgeon with a sharp eye, a cool head, and a steady hand will usually prefer to have the command of his patient's voluntary motions, and to avoid the danger which may arise from his restlessness on awaking from his drunken sleep."

Hulke, writing of his reminiscences of Sir William Bowman's work, said:

" In London, so far as my knowledge extends, Sir William Bowman was the first surgeon who employed chloroform in ' extraction.' In his first case the administration of chloroform was followed by vomiting after the completion of the operation—which could not have been more perfectly performed—and the violent straining induced choroidal hæmorrhage with extrusion of the vitreous humour and the retina through the corneal incision—the eye was lost. So serious a disaster would have deterred many men from the further trial of chloroform, but its advantages in respect of the performance of the operation were so manifest that Sir William Bowman persevered in its use, and in order to inspire confidence in his patients he experimentally inhaled it to complete anæsthesia himself. His conviction of its extreme usefulness in extraction was soon shared by others, and its employment quickly became general."

The practice as regards the use of chloroform at Moorfields Hospital during the first decade after its introduction is summed up in the following extract on the subject from the second edition of James Dixon's *Guide to the Practical Study of the Diseases of the Eye* :

" We may regard it under two aspects: as saving the patient from pain, and as facilitating the manipulations of the surgeon. Now, it is notorious that operations performed on the globe itself cause very little pain, and last but a very short time. Those on the lids, involving as they do the wounding of the skin, are of course more painful; but, in respect of the suffering they cause, none of these are comparable to the larger operations in General Surgery, and there are few adults who, if thoroughly informed as to the real nature of such operations as those for cataract, artificial pupil and strabismus or even entropion and ectropion in their slighter forms, will not readily undergo them without the aid of anæsthetics.

" A perfect passive condition of the eye is so desirable in the delicate operations of cataract and artificial pupil, that one would naturally expect to find chloroform universally applicable in such cases; and specially indicated in the most delicate of all—extraction. But this forms a peculiar and exceptional case, and for the following reasons: We have seen that—provided the operation has been properly performed—the successful result of an extraction chiefly depends upon the rapidity with which the union of the corneal wound can be effected. Now, with every precaution it will sometimes happen that chloroform induces vomiting, and the violent efforts which attend this might disturb the lips of the wound, and cause the vitreous body to escape between them, thus inducing a prolapse of the iris, with all its accompanying irritation and retarded union. But, without taking such an extreme case as this, we shall find a very serious objection to the use of chloroform in the fact, that the squeamishness and disrelish for food which it induces may interfere with the reparative process, by impairing the nutrition of the cornea during the critical twenty-four hours immediately following the operation.

" In adults who are extremely fearful and unsteady, chloroform may be required in the operations for artificial pupil and strabismus; it will always be indicated in cases of extirpation of the globe, and it may greatly facilitate the examination of eyes rendered irritable by disease or by the presence of foreign bodies.

" In children all these manipulations will be greatly facilitated by the use of chloroform, and some can hardly be performed at all without its aid."

White Cooper, who was a great friend and follower of Dalrymple, wrote in 1853 as follows:

" In common with many others, I for some time hesitated before using chloroform in extraction of cataract, from a fear that the object of the operation might be defeated by the eye receiving injury during the return of consciousness, or by vomiting afterwards. It appeared to me, however, so deserving of a trial that nearly two years ago I first employed it, and since that time have availed myself of it very frequently in operations on the eye, including 16 cases of extraction of cataract, 9 of artificial pupil, 4 of foreign body in the eyeball, and 2 of tumours of the globe, besides numerous needle cases.

" The advantage obtained by the use of chloroform in operations on the eye are a perfectly quiescent condition of the globe or the lids, absence of congestion of the eye, and mental tranquillity for the patient. To the operator the perfect repose of the eye affords a manifest advantage, the various steps of the operation being performed with as much facility as in a demonstration on the dead subject; the risk of prolapse of the iris (which is usually caused by muscular action) is greatly diminished, and the corneal flap can be accurately adjusted."

By improved methods of preparation of patients before the administration of chloroform the risks of vomiting became reduced. By a modification of the operation of extraction so that a piece of the iris was removed, either at the time of the extraction of the cataract or as a preliminary procedure, the risk of its protrusion into the wound was avoided; and by the modification of the opening made in the eye, so that it formed a straight linear incision instead of a flap, the risk of its gaping open subsequently was diminished. Ultimately, up to the time of the introduction of cocaine in 1884, the employment of chloroform for extraction of cataract became the general custom, and the performance of the operation without its aid the exception.

The following return of the number of cases to which chloroform was administered during the first six months in 1868 shows how general its use in operative procedures on the eye had then become: Cataract, 74; removal of eye, 67; iridectomy, 99; iriddesis, 11; syringe, 15; entropion and ectropion, 36; abscission, 5; strabismus, 166; tumours of lid and orbit, 8. Total, 481.

After the introduction of anæsthetics many new operative procedures on the eye were invented, and those formerly in use, like that of extraction of cataract, became modified and improved. In all these changes and advances Critchett and Bowman, at Moorfields Hospital, played a conspicuous part.

Excision of the eyeball was at one time a most formidable procedure, and was only resorted to in cases of malignant growths. Hulke has recorded the following graphic description of his recollections of it at the time of his pupillage:

" The first excision of the eyeball that I saw was to me, a novice, so horrible and distressing a scene that the impression it made still lingers in my recollection. No anæsthesia. The surgeon first passed through the eyeball a stout needle armed with stout silk, and knotting the ends, formed a loop. Next, with this he dragged forwards the eyeball, and then scooped it out of its socket with a double-edged scalpel curved on the flat of the blade. This done an assistant, who stood ready with a large brass clyster-syringe, checked the profuse bleeding by squirting into the orbit iced water. How different this from enucleation as now done—methodical circular division of the conjunctiva, severance of the muscles at their insertions into the globe, careful section of the optic nerve with scissors !"

The suggestion that the eyeball might thus neatly and safely be dissected out of its encircling capsule originated with an anatomist, O'Ferrall, in Dublin in 1841, and was first put into practice by Bonnet in France in the following year. George Critchett independently adopted it, and gave a description of the proceeding in 1851. After that, excision of the eye became an increasingly frequent operation for the relief of pain, when the sight was irretrievably destroyed, or for the improvement of appearances where the eye had become unsightly and disfiguring. The consequent increased demand for artificial eyes resulted in their improvement in construction and appearance. Their manufacture became a highly specialised art, and a Mr. Gray was appointed purveyor of artificial eyes to the Hospital.

In 1844 Lawrence wrote:

" The influence of one eye upon the other is not confined to cases of disease. When an eye has been lost by accident, the other often becomes diseased sooner or later, without any imprudence or any external influence that would be injurious under ordinary circumstances. This kind of occurrence is so common, that it is necessary to warn those who have lost an eye of this danger, and the necessary precautions for avoiding it."

PLATE XI.

George Critchett

[To face p. 86

The prophylactic treatment of removal of eyes injured in such a way as to provoke this sympathetic disease does not, however, seem to have been put into practice until 1854, when it was first adopted by Prichard of Bristol. So effectual did this prophylactic measure prove that it soon became generally adopted, and excision of the eyeball at Moorfields Hospital, from being a rarely performed operation, as it was in the pre-anæsthetic days, became one of the commonest operations.

The operation for squint, before the introduction of anæsthetics, was a very crude procedure, and was performed often in what seems to-day a very indiscriminate manner.

The patient was seated in an armchair with a high back, against which the head was fixed by an assistant who stood behind it. The same, or another assistant, held the eyelids apart. The operator, standing in front, exposed the muscle to be dealt with by making a long incision in the membrane overlying it. He then passed a curved grooved director beneath it, and divided the muscle by running a sharp-pointed bistoury, or knife, along the groove in the director, no special attention being paid as to whether the tendon or the muscle itself was cut across. Loss of mobility with an unsightly prominence of the eye not infrequently resulted; whilst the large, open wound which was left often developed a mass of granulation tissue which considerably delayed healing.

Through the ingenuity of George Critchett, a much neater and simpler procedure was devised, by which many of the disadvantages of the older method were obviated. Only a small opening was made in the conjunctiva, the whole proceeding for division of the tendon being carried on beneath it; a hook was inserted under the muscle in place of the director, and scissors were used to cut through the tendon close to its insertion into the eyeball.

Disorders arising in connection with the drainage apparatus for the passage of the tears from the eye to the nose have attracted the attention of those engaged in the healing art since very ancient times.   In 1833 Sir William Lawrence wrote that to give a description of all the proceedings which have been proposed for removing obstruction to the tear duct would fill a moderate volume, but that the greater part were obsolete.   The collection of all those which have been proposed since that date would fill a second volume. Amongst all these different methods of treatment, that devised by Bowman in 1851 of slitting up the openings into the tear sac at the inner angle of the eyelids, the lacrymal puncta and canaliculi, represented a considerable advance on those which had been previously employed.   He first practised it in cases of overflow of tears caused by closure or displacement of the lacrymal puncta; afterwards, in the treatment of obstruction of the nasal duct, he passed probes through the slit canaliculus to dilate the stricture in the duct, and introduced through it styles to be worn for a time in order to maintain the dilatation.   The introduction of styles worn in this way avoided the disfigurement entailed when, as formerly, they were introduced through the skin of the nose overlying the tear sac.

Gibson of Manchester (as mentioned in Chapter II.), independently of Saunders, introduced in 1811 a method of operating on cataracts in infants.   He first broke up the lens, and reduced it to a pulp, with a couching needle; then, two or three weeks later, evacuated it through a small incision in the cornea by the introduction of a curette.

This operation, though practised for some time in Manchester, fell into disuse.   At Moorfields, the Saunderian tradition was still adhered to, allowing the lens matter slowly to become dissolved in the fluids of the eye.   In 1851 Bowman revived and improved upon Gibson's operation, and in 1864, in the *Ophthalmic Hospital Reports*, T. Pridgin Teale, junr., described how, in order to aid the removal of softened lens matter, he had employed a suction curette.   The curette was converted into a tube by having its groove roofed over to within a line of its extremity; it was connected with an indiarubber tube, and the suction was made by the mouth of the operator. The idea of extraction by suction can, he said, "boast of considerable antiquity, as the following quotation, kindly sent me by Mr. Bowman, will show":

"According to Avicenna a similar proceeding (viz., excision of cataract, by opening in the cornea and drawing out the cataract by a needle) was practised by the Persians in the fourth century, and Albucasis reports that the procedure was gradually displaced by the ' suctions-method,' in which the cataract was sucked out through a hollow needle."

Bowman himself, later on, had constructed a suction apparatus for soft cataracts, which could be manipulated with one hand, the suction being made by the movement upwards of a piston with the thumb.

After the introduction of anæsthetics, which allowed of patients being kept perfectly quiet during the performance of operations on the eye, procedures requiring great precision and skill were introduced by both Bowman and Critchett for the formation of artificial pupils.

Bowman, in order to produce an enlargement of the pupil of a limited extent, in a suitable direction, whilst still keeping it as central as possible, made use of canula-scissors. These were scissors with delicate blades expanding from a stem which moved up and down in a canula, the size of a cataract needle, by means of a spring in the handle. When the spring was pressed the scissors were closed by being drawn partly into the canula, and when it was relaxed they opened, being protruded by the spiral wire. One blade of the scissors, which protruded beyond the other, was pointed with a sharp cutting edge capable of penetrating the cornea and allowing the whole of the closed scissors being introduced into the anterior chamber of the eye. The other shorter blade of the scissors was blunt-pointed. When within the eye, the blades of the scissors were opened and made to cut the pupillary border of the iris, the blunt-pointed blade being passed behind and the sharp-pointed one in front. The calibre of the canula was so graduated as to plug the wound through which it was introduced, and prevent the escape of the aqueous humour.

For use in other cases he had constructed a modified form of Tyrrell's hook. It was of the same size, but sharp and flattened at the point. Its stem was cylindrical so as exactly to occupy the corneal wound and prevent the escape of the aqueous humour. With this " needle hook," as he termed it, the necessity of making a preliminary incision with the loss of the aqueous humour, before the introduction of the hook, was avoided; the needle hook introduced itself into the eye, the retention of the aqueous humour facilitating the precision with which the hook could be passed round the pupillary border.

Critchett invented an operation which he called " irid-desis," or the formation of artificial pupil by tying the iris. The purpose of the procedure he described as follows:

" The formation of what is commonly called an artificial pupil is required under various morbid or abnormal conditions of the eye, and demands a corresponding variety in the modes by which it is accomplished. In some cases, a restoration of the original pupil as regards size and situation is all that is wanted; in others, a change in the size, shape, and situation of the natural pupil is required; or, again, it may be necessary to form a new pupil in an abnormal situation and in the very substance or tissue of the iris. In each of these different cases the object is the same—viz., to establish a clear pupil or aperture in the iris opposite to a transparent part of the cornea.

" It is very desirable that, in the formation of an artificial pupil, the conditions upon which the perfection of the natural pupil depends should be as nearly as possible preserved and imitated, both as regards its position and defined border, its size, mobility, and sensitiveness to light. In the methods usually employed these conditions are frequently unattainable, and the circular fibres of the natural pupil are either cut or torn through, and an opening is formed which is very probably large and irregular in shape, fixed and insensible to light, ill-defined and extending to the margin of the cornea—thus admitting rays of light that are too much refracted by the margin of the lens, and having the effect altogether of confusion of vision."

His operation, designed to overcome the disadvantages above mentioned, consisted in drawing into a wound at the margin of the cornea, with canula-forceps, a small piece of the periphery of the iris and fixing it there by tying a loop of silk around it. In this way an alteration of the position of the pupil was effected without its margin being cut or the sphincter muscle interfered with.

The operation was for some time extensively practised at Moorfields, not only by Critchett, but also by Bowman and Poland. In cases of conical cornea, Bowman, by performing this operation at the outer and inner margin of the cornea, produced a laterally elongated slit-like opening; in order to create the same beneficial visual effect, in such cases, as is sometimes derived by holding a slit-shaped opening in a metal disc in close proximity to the eye.

Later on, it was found that this ingenious operation of iriddesis was liable to be followed by inflammation in the eye of a type which might spread to the fellow eye: it became, therefore, entirely abandoned.

Another discovery which largely extended the range of operative ophthalmic surgery was that glaucoma could be relieved by the removal of a piece of the iris.

A. von Graefe first performed an operation of this description for glaucoma in Berlin in June, 1856. His study of the natural history of the disease, and of its ophthalmoscopical appearances, had led him to the conclusion that increased hardness, or tension, of the eyeball was the leading factor in its causation, and that, if some means could be devised of permanently lowering the tension, its cure might be effected. Experience had shown him that after the removal of a piece of the iris to form an artificial pupil, in eyes where the tension was increased, normal tension became restored. After having performed experimental iridectomies on animals' eyes, he felt justified in trying the effect of the operation on patients suffering from glaucoma, and with the most gratifying results. Up to that time the disease inevitably resulted in blindness, and in some of its forms was accompanied by the most agonising pain and distress. The discovery of a means whereby not only could the pain be relieved, but the loss of sight also prevented, must always be regarded as one of the greatest triumphs of ophthalmic surgery.

The successful performance of iridectomy for glaucoma requires a steadier hand and more skill than any other operation on the eye. It is also necessary to have the patient absolutely quiet. The acute pain to which the affection gives rise renders the eye exceedingly sensitive, and even to-day most surgeons prefer to perform it on patients under the influence of a general anæsthetic. Indeed, the introduction of inhalation anæsthesia may be said to have paved the way for the operative treatment of glaucoma.

1851 was the year of the first Great Exhibition in London, held in the Crystal Palace in Hyde Park. Visitors from all parts of the world flocked to see it, and amongst them came Albrecht von Graefe, then twenty-three years of age, full of enthusiastic ardour and fresh from his studies in the clinics of Germany, Vienna, and Paris; also Frans Cornelius Donders, thirty-three years of age, whom his friend Moleschott described with fervid admiration as " a swelling rosebud, whose calix leaves signified nothing but pure science; the flower leaves hidden glory. In one word, he was a man complete—perfect for his time of life." He was at that time Professor Extraordinary at the University of Utrecht, and lectured on no less than four subjects—viz., Forensic Medicine, Anthropology, General Biology, and Ophthalmology.

These two men and Sir William Bowman, destined to revolutionise the practice of ophthalmology, met for the first time in London in that eventful year, and remained on terms of the most intimate friendship for the rest of their lives. Donders and Bowman have left on record the following interesting descriptions of their first meeting; the first wrote:

" In August, 1851, at the International Exhibition, chance threw von Graefe and myself together in London. I had already enjoyed the companionship of Friedrich von Jaeger, when one morning a young man in Alpine costume rushed into Guthrie's eye hospital—he had reached London but two hours before—and threw himself into Jaeger's arms. With the words, ' You are made for each other,' the latter literally threw him into mine. And he was not mistaken. From early morning, when, on our way to Moorfields Hospital, we took our modest breakfast in Oxford Street amongst the workmen going to their work, till late evening, when we gratefully quitted the hospitable home of our friend William Bowman, we remained inseparably united in common objects of pursuit. Von Graefe was my guide in practical work, of which I had as yet but little experience, and I again could impart to him much from the physiological side. This mutual instruction constituted for us a great attraction. These days in which von Graefe unfolded the whole charm of his nature belong to the happiest recollections of my life."

Bowman, in describing Donders' visit to London that year, says:

" It was his first travel, and it brought him, at least, one thing for which he had great reason to be thankful—the personal friendship of Albrecht von Graefe, an association soon to be fraught with splendid results for the expanding science of ophthalmology; for these two men, both of the first capacity, laboured ever afterwards to advance it as brothers in council, and alike fruitfully; freely communicating their ideas to each other, always in perfect harmony of aim. While von Graefe, a stranger in London, was able to tell Donders of the European hospitals he had been visiting, and of the new clinical ideas he was maturing, as well as of the construction in that year, by Helmholtz at Königsberg, of a dioptric apparatus for rendering visible the fundus of the eye, Donders, a stranger there too, could on his side explain many discoveries of his own in the physiological field, and, amongst other things, declare the true nature of the act of accommodation, quite recently disclosed with certainty by his countryman Cramer, under, it may be added, his own inspiration and in his own laboratory."

Sir William Bowman at the time of this memorable meeting was older than his two friends, being thirty-five years of age.   His biographer wrote of him:

" At a period of life when most men are only beginning to apply their powers of observation and reflection, he, exercising both in a high degree, had already done work quite unexampled for its novelty, interest, variety, and above all for its accuracy.   Before attaining the age of twenty-six, he had won for himself a leading position amongst the most eminent anatomists of his time as a microscopist of first-rate ability, and the discoveries he had made, with the conclusions he drew from them, have ever since exercised an important influence in practical medicine, and have served as models for all subsequent and similar investigations.   Later in life he became distinguished as an original investigator in physiology, and as a teacher in that subject, and, at a still later period, devoting himself to a special branch of his profession, he stepped naturally and easily into the position of leader and representative of ophthalmic medicine and surgery, holding the same position in this country, though for a far longer period, that was occupied in Germany by his friend von Graefe, and in Holland by his still more intimate associate Donders."

As the immediate result of his histological work on muscle, Bowman was in 1841, at the unusually early age of twenty-five, elected a Fellow of the Royal Society.   At the Oxford meeting of the British Medical Association, in 1847, he read a paper entitled, " On some Points in the Anatomy of the Eye, chiefly in Reference to the Power of Adjustment,"

PLATE XII.

SIR WILLIAM BOWMAN, BART., F.R.S.

[To face p. 94

in which he demonstrated, simultaneously with and independently of Bruecke, the structure and function of the ciliary muscle.

In the same year, he delivered to the students at Moorfields Hospital a series of six lectures dealing with the parts concerned in operations on the eye and on the structure of the retina. They contained an account of his investigations into the microscopical anatomy of the eye, and were published in book form two years later, a book which ever since has been regarded as one of the classics of ophthalmology; a French translation of it by M. Testelin was published in the *Annales d'Oculistiques* in 1855.

Bowman's discovery of the ciliary muscle, bearing as it did on Donders' investigations on the accommodation of the eye, formed from the first a bond of intellectual union between the two men, which, with the growth of years, ripened into the warmest esteem and friendship. Donders wrote on the front leaf of his great work, *On the Anomalies of Accommodation and Refraction of the Eye* :

" To William Bowman, F.R.S., whose merits in the advancement of Physiology and Ophthalmology are equally recognised and honoured in every country, this work on the anomalies of refraction and accommodation is, in testimony of the warmest friendship and of the highest esteem, inscribed by the Author."

Though Graefe first performed the operation of iridectomy for glaucoma in June, 1856, it was not until the following year that he published an account of his great discovery. He wisely waited until he had tested it in the different varieties and stages of the disease until he gave an account of it to the world at large.

Dr. Bader, the curator and registrar at Moorfields, wrote in 1859:

" The first instance of glaucoma treated by excision of a portion of iris by von Graefe's method was in a case of chronic glaucoma, operated upon May 1st, 1857; a second case was treated in the same manner in October in the same year. Both were cases of chronic glaucoma in an advanced stage, and the immediate result for vision was not such as would recommend the operation. Then came several cases of acute and subacute glaucoma, in which a striking improvement followed shortly after the operation. Since then iridectomy has been tried extensively at Moorfields, and with good and lasting results in many cases."

In the second number of the *Ophthalmic Hospital Reports*, published in January, 1858, Critchett recorded some cases of acute glaucoma which he had treated successfully by iridectomy, though not quite in accordance with Graefe's method.

Some years later Bowman wrote the following description of the introduction of the operation into this country:

" Since the winter of 1856-7, the splendid researches of von Graefe on the nature and treatment of glaucoma have prominently attracted attention. On the Continent, his proposal to arrest the disease by the excision of a portion of the circle of the iris has been adopted and practised by the ablest men, including especially Professors Donders of Utrecht, Arlt of Vienna, and Desmarres of Paris. In May, 1857, I first performed it in England. At the Ophthalmological Congress at Brussels, in September following, von Graefe gave an account of his researches, and distributed amongst his friends an essay on the subject, then just presented to the French Institute. In the ensuing autumn, *iridectomy as a remedy for glaucoma* was, in my opinion, and in that of my friend and colleague, Mr. Critchett, established by the facts we had ourselves observed, as a proceeding competent to cope with the disease, by reducing that tension of the eyeball, and compression of the retina and its vessels, which is the cause of the loss of sight.

" It was our earnest wish that the value of von Graefe's discovery should be early and extensively acknowledged by medical men, so that those suffering from so serious a malady might no longer be drifting, as before, into hopeless blindness. Since then we have with no faltering voice continued to advocate the practice, and have performed the operation on all suitable occasions, both in private and in public.

At Moorfields, iridectomy has been exhibited and tested on a very large scale, scarcely a week having passed since 1858 without one or more instances of it; and a host of competent observers, both students and practitioners, have witnessed the method of performing it, and its results, in the hands of several of my colleagues and myself."

Both Critchett and Bowman began as general surgeons as well as ophthalmic surgeons. Critchett was appointed assistant-surgeon at the London Hospital in 1846, and became full surgeon in 1861. Bowman was appointed assistant-surgeon at King's College Hospital in 1840, and became full surgeon in 1856.

So extensive and absorbing became their work in ophthalmology that both of them ultimately found it necessary to resign their general surgical appointments and devote themselves exclusively to the treatment of eye diseases.

Their reputation as masters in their speciality was not confined to their own country, but became world-wide. George Critchett, who was an admirable French scholar, frequently attended the meetings of the International Ophthalmological Congress, and his son, Sir Anderson, was fond of relating how, at one of its meetings held in Paris in 1867, he performed the operation of extraction of cataract, before the assembled Congress, on the two eyes of a patient, using his right hand for the one eye and his left hand for the other. So great was his dexterity that at the conclusion of the operation, Graefe, who was presiding at the Congress, threw his arms round his neck and kissed him on both cheeks.

Both Critchett and Bowman were men with strong and attractive personalities, and collected around them at Moorfields not only a large body of students, but also practitioners who were devoting themselves to ophthalmology from all parts of the world. In 1859 they commenced to supplement their clinical teaching by giving a systematic three months' course of lectures on Ophthalmic Surgery, attendance at which course enabled students to comply with the rules of the Royal College of Surgeons for obtaining a certificate.

Most foreign missionaries from this country have endeavoured to promote the spread of Christianity by practising gratuitously the healing art. David Livingstone was a qualified medical man, and administered medical relief to large numbers of the African natives amongst whom he lived. From some remarks of Sir J. Risdon Bennett, with reference to Livingstone's medical studies in London in 1839, it seems probable that he was then in attendance at Moorfields Hospital. Many missionaries have not sufficient medical training to entitle them to practise in this country; but, when abroad, feel themselves called upon to administer such European drugs as they possess, having greater knowledge of their uses than the inhabitants of the district in which they are situated. It was to aid such persons to alleviate affections of the eye that the Committee of Management of the Hospital obtained the consent of the medical staff, in 1854—

" To admit gratuitously to the practice of the Hospital gentlemen qualified to derive advantage from it, by the possession of some amount of preliminary medical knowledge; provided they be duly authenticated to them by a Missionary Society or otherwise, as being about to proceed on missionary labours abroad."

A letter was then drawn up and printed, embodying this resolution, for circulation amongst those whom it might interest. Large numbers of missionaries, both men and women, have since availed themselves of the opportunities thus afforded them before taking up their duties abroad, and in this way the teaching and benefits of Moorfields have been spread to remote regions and to many uncivilised people.

CHAPTER VII

THE DISCOVERY OF THE OPHTHALMOSCOPE

THE two decades from 1850 to 1870 may well be described as the golden age of ophthalmology, on account of the many new discoveries and developments made in connection with it during that epoch.

In the last chapter the surgical improvements which were effected have been spoken of, together with the crowning achievement of them all—the introduction of the operation of iridectomy for the relief of glaucoma.

In this chapter will be described an event, destined not only to change the whole outlook of ophthalmology, but also to add a valuable means for the detection of disease in many of the organs and tissues of the body—the discovery of the ophthalmoscope. Following on its discovery, and to some extent incidental to it, came the recognition of the different forms of errors of refraction, and the building up of the methods for their correction with glasses, with which the name of Donders will for all time be associated.

The merit of discovering the ophthalmoscope, and of having given it to the world in 1851, belongs to Professor von Helmholtz, who, having commenced his career as an army surgeon, was, by his mathematical talents, led on from the study of physiology to that of physics, and to the production of his greatest work, his *Manual of Physiological Optics*.

The ophthalmoscope was, he said,

" a discovery rather than an invention; that is to say, when a well-trained physicist came and grasped the importance of such an instrument, nothing more was wanted, since all the knowledge had been developed which was required for its construction."

In speaking of his discovery in later years he said:

" The ophthalmoscope has unfolded itself to me simply out of the necessity of discussing, in my lectures on physiology, the theory of emission of light by the eye. Why does the human eye not glisten under ordinary circumstances, since in its background there is situated a spot— small, indeed, but clear white; that is to say, the end of the optic nerve, which must reflect light in the same way as the most sparkling tapetum of animals' eyes ? Why do animals' eyes sometimes shine with such remarkable lustre, though they may only be illuminated by a small distant flame ? These questions, when once proposed, were not difficult to answer, and now the answer is known to everybody. Once answered, they furnished the means of lighting up the eye of another human being, and of seeing it plainly."

It not infrequently happens, that when time is pregnant with some new discovery, more than one person is found to have been hopefully striving to become its accoucheur. So it was with the discovery of the ophthalmoscope. Here in England, in 1846, William Cumming, a young surgeon who was working at the Royal London Ophthalmic Hospital, had noticed that a reflex could be obtained from the fundus of the human eye under certain conditions of illumination. At the Medico-Chirurgical Society that year he read a paper entitled " On a Luminous Appearance of the Human Eye," the conditions for obtaining which he described as follows:

" (a) That the eye must be at some distance from the source of light, the distance being greater in proportion to the intensity; (b) that the rays of light diffused around the patient (and sometimes around the eye itself) should be excluded; (c) that the observer should occupy a position as near as possible to the direct line between the source of light and the eye examined."

With remarkable prospection he foreshadowed some of the results which were ultimately obtained from the use of the ophthalmoscope; thus he wrote:

" The establishment of the fact of a similar reflection from the human eye to that from the eyes of animals appears to be chiefly important in its adoption as a mode of examining the posterior part of the eye. The retina and choroid hitherto concealed in the living eye, and little opportunity being afforded of examining their condition after life, in consequence of their diseases not terminating fatally, considerable uncertainty had hitherto attended the diseases ascribed to these structures; but the existence of this luminosity, its non-existence, or abnormal appearance may enable us to detect changes in these structures hitherto unknown, or satisfactorily to see those which we only suspected.

" If we dilate the pupil with atropine, we have the means afforded of seeing the condition of the retina and choroid in every case. The cases I have examined in this way have confirmed the general impression that the retina is not frequently the seat of changes in amaurosis; for, out of several cases of amaurosis, in which the non-opacity of the cornea, lens, and humours allowed this mode of examination, I found but two in which the retina was so changed that the reflection was not seen."

Cumming discussed these matters with Dixon and Bowman, the latter suggesting to him that the choroid and its pigment was probably the reflecting surface. Another quotation from his article will show how near he actually came to the discovery of the ophthalmoscope; thus he wrote:

" On approaching within a few inches of the eye the reflection is not visible, for, before our eye can be brought within range of the reflected rays, the incident rays are excluded."

Cumming died in 1855, at the early age of thirty-three, but just lived sufficiently long to see that what he had foretold was being realised. In 1862 a portrait in oil-colours of him was presented to the Hospital by one of his relatives with the following letter:

" 2, Vittoria Place, Limehouse,

" *November 11th*, 1862.

" Sir,

" I have the pleasure of presenting to the Hospital a portrait of the late William Cumming of Limehouse. It is from a painting in possession of the family.

" William Cumming was honourably connected with the Institution, was discoverer that the fundus of the living eye could be explored, and a pioneer in the recent advances in Eye Surgery.

" He died in 1855 at the early age of 33 years.

" I am, etc.,

" John Stewart Cumming."

This portrait still hangs in the Board Room of the Hospital.

In 1847 Charles Babbage, a distinguished mathematician and scientific mechanician, who held the Lucasian Chair of Mathematics at Cambridge, and who spent a large part of his life in the construction of a calculating machine, actually invented an ophthalmoscope. He himself published no description of it, and we know nothing of the circumstances which led up to this invention; the only record we have concerning it is that published by Wharton Jones in 1854, in a " Report on the Ophthalmoscope " in the *Medico-Chirurgical Review*. He wrote:

" It is but justice that I should here state, however, that seven years ago Mr. Babbage showed me the model of an instrument that he had contrived for the purpose of looking into the interior of the eye. It consisted of a bit of plain mirror, with the silver scraped off at two or three spots in the middle, fixed within a tube at such an angle that the rays of light, falling on it through the side of the tube, were reflected to the eye to be observed, and to which one end of the tube was directed. The observer looked through the clear spot of the mirror from the other end."

Probably Wharton Jones, who was himself short-sighted, in using Babbage's reflecting mirror, without any lens, only obtained a red glow from the fundus of the eye, and saw

PLATE XIII.

WILLIAM CUMMING.
From a painting in the Board Room of the Hospital.

[To face p. 102

nothing of the optic nerve or of the retinal bloodvessels, for, had he done so, it seems unlikely that a man of his powers of observation and scientific attainments would not have realised the possibilities of such an instrument.

Anyhow, he gave Babbage no encouragement, and the instrument was laid aside as a mere toy.

Indeed, it seems doubtful if Helmholtz himself at first fully realised the possibilities of his great discovery. On the occasion of the presentation to him of the first Graefe medal in Heidelberg in 1886, Donders spoke as follows:

" How the ophthalmoscope could be serviceable to ophthalmologists, how the eye under examination, whilst its fundus becomes visible, constitutes for the emmetropic examiner a lens, too weak in myopia, in hypermetropia too strong; and how simultaneously with the examination of the fundus, the refraction can be determined; all this was clearly indicated by von Helmholtz. But he never thought, or at least he never said, that the new instrument implied the dawning of a new era for ophthalmology. Von Graefe felt it immediately. When he, for the first time, saw the background of the eye, with its nerve-entrance and its bloodvessels, his cheeks reddened, and he called out excitedly: ' Helmholtz has unfolded to us a new world,' and then, ' What remains there to be discovered?' added he thoughtfully.

" It was, indeed, humiliating to hear it said, banteringly, that black cataract was that disease in which the patient saw nothing, nor the surgeon either. Treatment was then but a groping in the dark. Under the same name were thrown together the most diverse affections of the fundus oculi and of the nerve apparatus; and even disturbances of refraction and accommodation, such as astigmatism and muscular asthenopia, were reckoned with amblyopia. And, against these most diverse disturbances, the same empirical remedies were employed—many of them a real torment to the patient—not only with little beneficial result, but sometimes at the cost of health."

The increasing number of operative procedures performed at the Hospital, and the coming of the ophthalmoscope, created a demand for more accommodation in both the in- and out-patient departments. The alterations necessary to supply these wants extended over several years, but ultimately resulted in the transference of the out-patient department, together with the dispensary and a dark room for ophthalmoscopic work, to newly erected buildings on the site of the Saunderian Institute, and the yard at the back of the main building. The ground floor of the latter was then utilised for rooms for the resident staff and for a committee room, and the first floor was turned into wards for in-patients.

Battley having ceased his pharmaccutical investigations and teaching, and Dr. Farre his pathological researches, they consented to hand over all their rights in the Saunderian Institute so that it might be made use of by the Hospital.

Shortly before Tyrrell's death, the Committee of Management had under consideration the hardship of an assistant-surgeon remaining on the staff for a number of years without the opportunity of gaining experience in performing the major operations on the eye. When Tyrrell died, both Mackmurdo and Dalrymple became full surgeons, and the matter was left for a time in abeyance. In 1854, however, at a meeting of the Governors, the rules were altered so that—

" any assistant-surgeon who shall have served the Hospital five years shall, provided he be a Fellow of the College of Surgeons, become, if the Committee think fit, a surgeon."

At the same time the title of the resident medical officer was changed from apothecary to house surgeon.

In 1854 the Crimean War commenced; its immediate effect on the Hospital was a reduction in its receipts from donations and subscriptions, which together amounted to £614 in 1853, and only to £236 in 1854. A Jubilee dinner to commemorate the fiftieth anniversary of the foundation of the Hospital was abandoned, and the building operations of the new out-patient department postponed.

PLATE XIV.

JAMES DIXON.

JOHN CAWOOD WORDSWORTH.

[To face p. 105

In 1855 Wordsworth, the junior assistant-surgeon, answered Mr. Sydney Herbert's call for volunteers in aid of the overtaxed military medical officers in the East, and, having obtained leave of absence from the Committee of Management, went as surgeon to the Civil Hospital at Smyrna. Later he was transferred to the Crimea, which he reached just in time to render good service " in the front " to those wounded in the attack upon the Redan. For three months of the following winter he was attached to the Castle Hospital on the heights above Balaclava.

On the conclusion of the war, at the annual general meeting of the Governors, the following resolutions were passed:

" That this meeting, holding in the highest respect and esteem the humane and benevolent consideration and sympathy manifested for the Army in the East, during the late War with Russia, by the Right Honourable Sydney Herbert, M.P., respectfully requests Mr. Herbert to accept the nomination of Honorary Life Governor and Vice-President of this Hospital.

" That this meeting appreciates most highly the humane and benevolent ministrations of Miss Florence Nightingale to the sick and wounded in the service of the country in the East during the late War with Russia, and it is hereby resolved that Miss Nightingale be a Life Governor of this Hospital."

Miss Nightingale and Mr. Sydney Herbert both replied accepting with pleasure these nominations.

Though Miss Nightingale was made a Life Governor of the Hospital, it was not until many years later that the reforms in the system of sick nursing, which she was instrumental in bringing about, were introduced at Moorfields.

In 1859, in consequence of the increased accommodation for in-patients, it was arranged that there should be a nurse with an assistant on each of the two floors. It was also ordered " that in future every patient on admission to the wards be bathed, unless otherwise ordered by the admitting officer." But that much was left to be desired in the matter of nursing will be gathered from a note directed to the Committee by the Medical Council in 1861, in which it requested the Committee to consider the advisability of providing proper receptacles for keeping the in-patients' clothes, " which are now generally put under the bedding, the consequence of which is that the beds occasionally get infested with vermin, to the serious discomfort of the patients who subsequently occupy them."

In 1856 Dr. Frederick Farre, who had become full physician at St. Bartholomew's Hospital, found that pressure of work necessitated his resigning his post on the active staff at Moorfields. His father, Dr. J. R. Farre, at the same time withdrew from his position of consulting physician, and Dr. Frederick Farre was appointed in his place. The family's connection with the Hospital was still further maintained by the appointment of Dr. J. R. Farre's younger son, Dr. Arthur Farre, a distinguished physician accoucheur, as a member of the Committee of Management.

Dr. Robert Martin, an assistant-physician at St. Bartholomew's Hospital, being the only candidate, was elected physician.

In the same year Gilbert Mackmurdo, who had served on the staff of the Hospital for a period of thirty-six years, resigned and was appointed consulting surgeon. The appointment of a new assistant-surgeon to fill the vacancy thus created gave rise to a most keenly contested election, in which 458 Governors recorded their votes. One of the daily papers, describing the event, stated " that the usually quiet neighbourhood of Finsbury was the scene of great excitement."

There were four candidates, and, at the close of the poll, the scrutineers announced that the votes had been distributed as follows:

Mr. J. S. Gamgee ..	..	..	..	3
Mr. J. W. Hulke ..	..	..	..	148
Mr. J. F. Streatfield	..	..	..	214
Mr. Walter Tyrrell	..	..	..	93

This method of election by Governors of the members of the medical staff was the general practice at most hospitals at that time; but though it helped to increase the funds of those institutions, it was not well calculated to secure the services of the most suitable candidate, and, as we shall see later, was subsequently abandoned.

The Governors consisted of " Life Governors "—*i.e.*, those who had contributed ten guineas in the course of one year, and annual subscribers of one guinea. A body of electors so formed was not well qualified to judge of the relative merits of rival candidates; and a candidate, with a number of friends willing to promote his interests by becoming subscribers, might thereby bring about a preponderating influence in his favour. Moreover, where more than two candidates presented themselves, the successful candidate might, as in this 1856 election, be elected without having received a majority of the votes recorded.

With an electorate of between 400 and 500 Governors, a candidate who set out to canvass them had a formidable task before him, and one which often proved an expensive proceeding. The last surgeon elected to the staff in this way estimated his costs at nearly £100, which seems an inordinate amount to expend for obtaining the privilege of giving one's time and service to the relief of the poor and needy. It can, therefore, be easily understood why a candidate, who found his chances of election doubtful, frequently withdrew in favour of one of the others, and contented himself with announcing his intention of applying again on a future occasion.

John Fremlyn Streatfield was the son of a well-known antiquarian, the Rev. Thomas Streatfield, of Charts Edge, Westerham, Kent. He inherited his father's antiquarian instincts and was also a staunch Churchman. He studied medicine at the London Hospital, and, like several of the other oncoming surgeons at Moorfields, served in the East at one of the British hospitals during the Crimean War.

In 1862 he was appointed assistant ophthalmic surgeon at the University College Hospital, and shortly afterwards, on the retirement from the staff there of Wharton Jones, succeeded him as full surgeon.

Streatfield was gifted with remarkable manipulative dexterity, and delighted in using his fingers in a way which most people would have regarded as impracticable. There was, indeed, something almost acrobatic in his method of operating, and George Critchett used jokingly to remark that he expected one day, on going into the operating theatre, to find Streatfield removing a cataract whilst at the same time he balanced a feather on his nose.

On the death of Earl Fitzwilliam, in 1857, the post of President of the Hospital became vacant, and Mr. William Cotton, D.C.L., F.R.S., an eminent merchant and philanthropist, having consented to be nominated for the post, was elected by the Governors. He was at one time Governor of the Bank of England, and invented a most ingenious machine, which has ever since been in use, for weighing sovereigns at the rate of twenty-three per minute; it is capable of discriminating to a ten-thousandth part of a grain, discharging the full-weight and the under-weight into different compartments. He was, perhaps, even more noted for his philanthropy than his ingenuity: he founded several churches and gave assistance to many charitable institutions.

At the same time H.R.H. the Duke of Cambridge was invited to become a Patron of the Hospital, which invitation he most graciously accepted.

As the medical staff became enlarged, its members formed themselves into a " Medical Council," to give collective consideration to matters referred to it by the Committee of Management, or to initiate measures for promoting the prosperity of the Hospital and the progress of ophthalmology.

In 1857, when several regulations and practices which

had been introduced were being codified, the following rule became included amongst those governing the Institution:

" The physicians, if any, surgical officers, with the consulting physicians and consulting surgeons, if any, shall constitute a Medical Board empowered to consult on all matters connected with the medical department, with the admission and conduct of pupils, and shall report to the Committee from time to time."

In 1856 this Medical Council made the following proposal to the Committee which led to the establishment of the posts of clinical assistants:

" That with a view to aid in treating the less important cases, to assist the clinical work of the out-patient room, and in case-taking, it might be worthy of the consideration of the Committee, whether advantage might not be taken of the zeal and knowledge of some of the younger surgeons attending the Hospital, by electing them for a period of six or twelve months, as assistants to the surgeons. The Committee might appoint such assistants to any of the surgeons who might require aid. They should be qualified to practise, and of such established character that perfect confidence could be placed in them for the steady performance of their duties. Many of these men, after completing their term of office, would carry skill to various parts of the country in which they settle, while from them the Governors would be gradually furnished with highly competent candidates for the vacancies which from time to time occur in the staff. Their title might be that of ' clinical assistants,' and they would be entitled on retirement to a superior certificate."

These recommendations of the Medical Council were put into practice, and have continued ever since to work out in the ways which it had forecast. The first clinical assistants to be appointed were Mr. J. W. Hulke, Mr. Jonathan Hutchinson, and Mr. Walter Tyrrell; and a year or so later, Mr. G. Lawson, Mr. Harkness, Mr. Hughlings Jackson, Mr. J. S. Wells, and Mr. J. Couper.

The following rule with regard to these appointments became embodied in the laws of the Hospital in 1861:

" That the appointment of clinical assistants be held for one year, and that these officers be annually re-eligible when approved by the Medical Council and sanctioned by the Committee of Management."

The increasing number of eyes which were removed for the relief of pain, on account of disfigurement, to prevent inflammation spreading to the fellow eye, or on account of the presence of a new growth, supplied a large amount of material for pathological investigation, and for the formation of a museum of pathological specimens.

When the Saunderian Institute was converted into a waiting room for out-patients, a room was set apart elsewhere for a museum and library; and with some of the money left over from the Saunderian Fund a microscope was purchased. In 1857 Dr. Charles Bader, a young German skilled in the use of the ophthalmoscope, was appointed curator and registrar, with an annual honorarium of 25 guineas.

The increasing interest excited in the various changes in the fundus of the eye revealed by the ophthalmoscope made it desirable to have a collection of water-coloured drawings depicting them for preservation in the museum. An artist, Mr. Schweizer, was employed to make such drawings under the superintendence of Bader. A long list of those which he produced is recorded in the early numbers of the *Ophthalmic Hospital Reports*, where also some of them are published in lithographic plates. The changes represented are all drawn on a very small scale, the pictures themselves only measuring $1\frac{1}{4}$ inches in diameter. They are, however, very faithful representations of the changes shown, and contain a remarkable amount of fine detail. There can be little doubt that Mr. Schweizer must himself have been shortsighted.

The interpretation of the nature of the changes revealed

PLATE XV.

GEORGE LAWSON.

JOHN WHITAKER HULKE, F.R.S.

[To face p. 111

by the ophthalmoscope called for much careful dissection and microscopical investigation. The two chief pioneers in this work at Moorfields were Hulke and Bader. The former, in an article on the morbid anatomy and pathology of the choroid and retina in 1857, wrote:

" Since the discovery of the ophthalmoscope great advances have been made in our knowledge of the diseases of the deeper parts of the eyeball. We are daily becoming more familiar with the morbid appearances which characterise the various affections of the choroid, the retina, the vitreous humour, and the lens. We read these appearances during life, as if portrayed upon the pages of a book; but our knowledge of them, of their exact situation and precise natures, must remain very imperfect without the explanation afforded by dissections and the microscope. The extensive practice of the Moorfields Ophthalmic Hospital has, by the liberality of the medical staff, for a long time afforded me great opportunities for working with the ophthalmoscope, and for making microscopical examinations of diseased eyeballs immediately after their removal."

In 1859 the Royal College of Surgeons chose as the subject for the Jacksonian Prize Essay of that year:

" The morbid changes in the retina as seen in the eye of the living person, and after removal from the body, together with the symptoms associated with several morbid conditions."

John Whitaker Hulke's essay was awarded the prize, and he subsequently published it in a somewhat altered form as a handbook to the use of the ophthalmoscope.

Hulke, who was born in 1830, was educated at the Moravian College at Neuwied, and became a fluent German linguist; he studied medicine at King's College Hospital, where he early became associated with Bowman. During the Crimean War he was attached to the hospitals at Smyrna and Sebastopol. In 1857 he was appointed assistant-surgeon to King's College Hospital, and in 1858, when an additional post of assistant-surgeon was created at Moorfields, he was elected unopposed, the only other candidate, Jonathan Hutchinson, retiring in his favour. In 1862 he transferred his services as a general surgeon to the Middlesex Hospital, where he became full surgeon in 1870. In 1867 he was elected a Fellow of the Royal Society for his researches relating to the anatomy and physiology of the retina in man and the lower animals, particularly the reptiles.

Hulke not only distinguished himself as a general surgeon, an ophthalmologist, a pathologist, but also as a geologist; he contributed several papers to the Royal Society on Palæontology, more especially in connection with the great extinct land reptiles (Dinosauria) of the secondary period. In 1887 he was presented the Walleston Medal, the greatest honour in the power of the Royal Society to bestow.

To those familiar with an Ophthalmic Hospital at the present time, it is difficult to conceive of its work being carried on without the devotion of much time and attention to the correction of errors of refraction with glasses. Yet it was only during the latter part of the nineteenth century that the scientific principles for the correction of such errors became recognised.

Hulke, in some reminiscences of his youth, remarked:

" In my earliest student days the ophthalmoscope was unknown, and errors of refraction were so little understood that a small tortoise-shell case, which could be easily carried in the trousers pocket, containing half a dozen convex and concave spherical lenses, was held to comprise a sufficient stock for every trial."

The simultaneous but independent discovery by Bowman and Bruecke of the muscular nature of what was formerly known as the ciliary ligament, the change in the form of the lens in accommodation demonstrated by Cramer, and the discovery of the ophthalmoscope by Helmholtz, prepared the way for Donders' great work, *On the Anomalies of Accommodation and Refraction of the Eye*, which was published in English by the New Sydenham Society in 1864.

James Ware, to whom reference has already been made, was one of the first surgeons in England to devote himself specially to the treatment of eye diseases (*vide* Chapter I., p. 11). He is entitled, Donders says, to be described as the discoverer of hypermetropia or long-sightedness. In a paper on " Observations Relative to the Near and Distant Sight of Different Persons," which Ware read before the Royal Society in 1812, he said:

" There are also instances of young persons, who have so disproportionate a convexity of the cornea or crystalline, or of both, to the distance of these parts from the retina, that a glass of considerable convexity is required to enable them to see distinctly, not only near objects, but also those that are distant; and it is remarkable that the same glass will enable many such persons to see both near and distant objects, thus proving that the defect in their sight is occasioned solely by too small a convexity in one of the parts above-mentioned, and that it does not influence the power by which their eyes are adapted to see at distances variously remote. In this respect such persons differ from those who had the crystalline humour removed by an operation, since the latter always require a glass to enable them to discern distant objects, different from that which they use to see those that are near."

These early and accurate observations of Ware's were forgotten, and it was not until 1859, at a meeting at Heidelberg, that Donders first clearly differentiated long-sightedness, or over-sightedness as some then termed it, from presbyopia, and suggested the term " hypermetropia " as an appropriate name for it. The importance of understanding correctly the nature of this affection of the eye was summed up thus by Donders:

" He who knows by experience how commonly hypermetropia occurs, how necessary a knowledge of it is to the correct diagnosis of the various defects of the eye, and how deeply it affects the whole treatment of the oculist, will come to the sad conviction that an incredible number of patients have been tormented with all sorts of remedies and have been given over to painful anxiety, who would have found immediate relief and deliverance in suitable spectacles."

What is termed " asthenopia," or tiredness of the eyes with confusion of vision after close work, without any alteration in their external appearance, had been attributed to a variety of causes by different observers. Lawrence spoke of it as an affection of the retina from excessive employment. Tyrrell endeavoured to prove that it was due to congestion of the choroid. It became recognised that it was not caused by contrasts of light and shade:

> " All day the vacant eye without fatigue
> Strays o'er the heaven and earth; but long intent
> On microscopic arts, its vigour fails."

That it was produced by application of the eyes to near objects suggested that the muscles that move the eyeballs might be concerned, and some even practised tenotomy of them for its relief. It was not until Donders demonstrated its association with hypermetropia that the circumstances under which it may arise were made clear, and the way shown in which it could be relieved by the use of spectacles.

Though we are indebted to Kepler for the earliest knowledge of short-sight, or myopia, it was not until after the discovery of the ophthalmoscope that the peculiar changes in the fundus of the eye associated with it, and due to enlargement of the posterior part of the eyeball, became recognised. At Moorfields they were described and pictured by Bader in the *Ophthalmic Hospital Reports* in 1858.

The elongation of the visual axis in myopic eyes, formed at the expense of the posterior wall, was first demonstrated by dissection by Arlt in Vienna in 1856.

The asymmetry of the dioptric system of the eye which we call astigmatism was first observed by that versatile genius, Thomas Young, in his own eyes in 1793; and later by Airy, the Astronomer Royal, in 1827, who introduced the use of cylindrical lenses for its correction. Airy's colleague, Whewell, suggested the term "astigmatism." That it was due to a difference in the curvature of the cornea in its two meridians was asserted by Wharton Jones in 1855 and by Wilde of Dublin. It was, however, Donders who by measurement first certainly proved that such asymmetry of the cornea actually existed.

The introduction of systematic sight-testing for errors of refraction at Moorfields was of gradual growth. In 1860 J. Soelberg Wells, who was then working there as a clinical assistant, wrote as follows:

" There are perhaps few subjects connected with ophthalmic practice which demand greater care and exactitude than the choice of a pair of spectacles. The very frequency with which we are called upon to improve vision by means of glasses is but too apt to make us somewhat careless and empirical in our mode of selection, and to prescribe those which the patient himself most fancies, even although they may not quite accord with the range of his accommodation, or with the scientific principles which should influence our choice. But how much more does not this inefficiency in selecting spectacles obtain among quasi-opticians, jewellers, etc. This is doubtlessly often attended with the most disastrous results, and eyes, which might with proper glasses have lasted for a number of years, are soon recklessly and unwittingly destroyed through ignorance and carelessness of unscientific opticians. In order to obviate this, I would urgently advise the adoption of a method practised in many parts of the Continent. In Berlin, for instance, von Graefe has spectacle boxes, containing convex and concave glasses (whose number corresponds exactly with those kept by the opticians); from these he selects the proper glasses, and puts the number of their focal distance on a slip of paper, which the patient takes to an optician, who supplies him with the spectacles thereon prescribed.

" I am fully aware that this proceeding would, at present, be carried out with some difficulty in England, owing to the fact that different opticians often number their glasses differently; but I have no doubt, that if the leading opticians would adopt a certain standard, the others would soon follow their example."

In order to overcome the difficulties caused by the inaccurate dispensing of glasses, it was agreed in 1861, on the recommendation of the Medical Council, to appoint Thomas Doublet, optician, of 7, City Road, Finsbury Square, the official optician to the Hospital. This appointment led to a letter of protest from William Hawes, optician, of 79, Leadenhall Street, in which he said that for the past twenty years he had been supplying spectacles ordered by the surgeons to patients of the Hospital at an agreed price. It is interesting to note this, as his son, Alfred Hawes, was later on appointed optician to the Hospital, an appointment which William's grandson still holds.

The system then in vogue for numbering lenses was the " inch system," the unit on which it was based being a lens having a principal focal distance of 1 inch. It was inconvenient, as it necessitated the refractive power of any lens of a weaker strength being expressed by a fraction, whose denominator represented its principal focal distance. Complications also arose owing to the variations of the inch in different countries. Thus in ordering glasses it was necessary to state if the trial lenses employed were graduated in English, Paris, or Prussian inches. It was Nagel in 1866 who proposed a metre system of numbering lenses—i.e., taking a lens with the principal focal distance of 1 metre as the unit, and speaking of it as having the refractive power of 1 diopter. The advantages of this new system soon became evident, and, after it had been considered and reported on favourably at the International Congress of Ophthalmology in 1872, its adoption became general.

Letters or figures have always been employed by ophthalmologists as the most convenient method for testing the power of vision. Alfred Smee, F.R.S., surgeon to the

Bank of England and to the Central London Ophthalmic Hospital, in a book entitled *Vision in Health and Disease ; the Value of Glasses for its Restoration and the Mischief caused by their Abuse*, the first edition of which was published in 1847, gave a series of graduated sized prints for the testing of vision, and described an optometer he had constructed for " the adaption of glasses."

Ed. von Jaeger of Vienna, in 1854, published a series of typographical specimens, distinguishing the various sizes of the letters by numbers instead of technical names, which allowed of their use by all nations. These have ever since remained the most generally used test for near vision. It was Snellen of Utrecht, however, who first constructed test types on a definite scientific principle, so that the strokes composing the letters are all drawn on a regularly proportional scale of thickness, the letters exhibiting themselves under an angle of five minutes at the distance at which they should normally be seen.

In 1860 the Committee of Management of Moorfields, at the request of the Medical Council, had drawn up and printed test types for use in the out-patient room.

By the death of Mr. Richard Heathfield in 1859 the Hospital lost one of its oldest supporters, who had been a friend of Saunders and associated with him in its foundation. When the Rev. J. Russell retired from the Chairmanship of the Committee of Management, Heathfield had succeeded him, and was a vigorous promoter of the extensions of the institution rendered necessary by the advance of knowledge.

Mr. F. G. Sambrooke was appointed Chairman in his place.

On the death of Miss Marian Sedgwick, the last surviving daughter of the late Harry Sedgwick, in January, 1860, the Hospital came into possession of the reversion bequeathed by him (as mentioned in Chapter III.) of the sum of £19,841 Three per Cent. Stock, subject to 10 per cent.

legacy duty. A portrait of this early supporter and munificent benefactor of the Charity had been previously presented by his family, and now hangs in the Board Room. In 1853 the Committee had commissioned Mr. Henry Weekes to construct a marble bust of Mr. Harry Sedgwick at the cost of £120, to be designed as a companion to that by the same artist of J. Cunningham Saunders. These two busts, together with that of Dalrymple, now adorn the entrance hall of the present building.

CHAPTER VIII

THE COMMENCEMENT OF " THE OPHTHALMIC HOSPITAL REPORTS "

THE first English journal devoted specially to the subject of ophthalmology originated with the medical staff of the Moorfields Hospital. The first number of the *Ophthalmic Hospital Reports*, as the journal was called, was published in October, 1857. Its origin and aims were set forth as follows:

" At a meeting of the Medical Council of the Hospital, on the 25th of August last, it was determined to issue a periodical record of ophthalmic observation and experience; it was thought that, not only at Moorfields, much valuable information was gained and lost that should be preserved, and that such a journal might obtain favour throughout the country. Mr. Streatfield was appointed to collect and arrange, from time to time, the material and order its publication.

" The Ophthalmic Journal will be, for the present, issued quarterly. It will give short monographs, by members of the staff, and of the profession generally (if we are so fortunate as to engage their attention), on any physiological or pathological subjects connected with our especial study; with, it is hoped, occasional engravings, or photographs, as illustrations. It will also contain a summary reprint of the monthly reports of the Registrar of the Hospital, and titles of books and preparations presented to the Ophthalmic Library and Museum of the Hospital. It will not contain reviews of books as such, or any correspondence, or anonymous publications. The opinions expressed in it must be understood to be those of individual authors. The editor will collect minor noteworthy observations, and record novelties and illustrative cases, with regard to consecutive detail."

A list of the subscribers given in the fifth part, published a year later, shows them to have then numbered 195. By its establishment the Library at the Hospital became enriched, for exchanges were effected between it and several other journals dealing directly or indirectly with ophthalmology.

Though the highly specialised subject of the journal prevented it from gaining a very extensive circulation, it became the medium for publication of original articles which are now regarded as among the classics of ophthalmic science.

The first volume is composed of six parts, published at intervals between October, 1857, and January, 1859. The first part opened with an article by Bowman, giving an extended account of his investigations into the treatment of lacrymal obstruction by slitting up the lacrymal punctum and the use of probes, which has already been referred to in Chapter VI. Poland also commenced a series of articles, which were continued in subsequent parts, on " Protrusion of the Eyeball." They contain a number of well recorded cases with interesting remarks, giving a vivid description of the treatment of inflammatory affection in pre-antiseptic days, by what was termed " antiphlogistic measures." In the third volume of the *Reports* Poland contributed an article on " Medico-legal Observations in Connection with Lesions of the Eye." Much has been written on this subject since, but little has been added, as regards matters in this country, which is not dealt with by Poland. He quotes Mr. Harry Bodkin Poland, barrister-at-law, no doubt a relative of his, as stating the legal position in the assessment of damages for accidents to be as follows:

" There is no fixed mode of assessing damages from accident. When it can be shown that a particular person is liable for causing an accident, etc., the jury decide as to the amount of damages to which the injured person is entitled, and neither the medical man nor the lawyer interferes, except to put before the jury the real nature of the injuries inflicted."

The following precautionary remarks, which he wrote some seventy years ago, evidently as the outcome of his experiences at Moorfields, are so applicable to-day that they may well be quoted:

" The causes which may lead to the loss of an eye through carelessness and negligence ought well to be borne in mind by the thoughtless, so that should any person be employed in any of the following acts, he should pay due regard to the passers-by, or those standing near, and thus obviate any necessity for rendering himself liable for the damages committed.

" The carrying or whirling about of sticks, umbrellas, guns, etc., in the public thoroughfares, the slashing about of whips, the careless use of the line and rod in fishing, the letting off of fireworks, the shooting of arrows, the throwing of missiles such as stones, lime, etc.; the chipping of wood, stone, and metals in the public highways, without adequate protection; the playing at tip-cat; the uncorking of effervescing draughts; the explosion of chemicals and gunpowder; and numerous other acts each and all of which have caused the loss of an eye or of both, and have been the means of litigation."

In 1861 Alfred Poland was elected surgeon to Guy's Hospital with charge of the large ophthalmic department, and, in accepting the appointment, was required by the Governors of Guy's to resign his post of surgeon at Moorfields, which he did most reluctantly. Many competent observers described him as the best operator on the eye they had ever seen. He was a spare, thin man, and made remarkable recoveries from several severe illnesses, but died ultimately of consumption at the age of fifty-two. The following account of some of his other characteristics have been recorded by one of his colleagues at Guy's:

" Poland had a remarkable power of gathering together detailed knowledge, including dry facts and figures, so that his essays are complete treatises on the subjects in hand, and are of permanent value.

" It was said with great truth that if Poland had been shut in a room containing not a single book, but with only pens and paper, he could have written a complete work on surgery, not in a vague way, giving merely general descriptions and treatment, but in a systematic manner, detailing the distinct forms and varieties of the disease then in his mind.

" He was utterly careless as to his personal appearance. He would leave the dissecting room without changing his coat, and it was often the subject of surmise whether he washed his hands.

" On his appointment to the surgeoncy at Guy's, the Treasurer had no hesitation in telling him he would have to dress himself more decently and cleanly. It is not, therefore, surprising that Poland never had any practice to speak of. There was nothing in his manner to give confidence, but he was a great favourite with students.

" His marriage a few years before his death was a misalliance, and added much to his misfortunes."

One of the most conspicuous features of the *Reports* since their commencement has been the contributions made to them by the several occupants in succession of the post of curator of the Museum, beginning with Charles Bader. This post has afforded the holders of it a most valuable field for pathological research, as all the eyes removed by the members of the staff are entrusted to the curator for his investigation, and often also a large number of specimens from elsewhere. The articles written by the several curators contain most of the valuable original work which has been done in this country on the subject.

In the fourth part of the journal, published in July, 1858, Jonathan Hutchinson, who was then working as a clinical assistant at the Hospital, commenced his ever memorable series of articles " On the Different Forms of Inflammation of the Eye consequent on Inherited Syphilis." In these articles he first definitely established the connection of

PLATE XVI.

SIR JONATHAN HUTCHINSON, F.R.S.

[To face p. 123

interstitial keratitis with inherited syphilis, and showed its frequent connection with certain characteristics of the complexion and physiognomy, and with peculiarities in the formation of the permanent teeth. Which latter are now universally known as " Hutchinson's teeth."

Jonathan Hutchinson was born in Yorkshire in 1828, of Quaker ancestors. For four years he studied at the York School of Medicine, and then came to London, when he attended at St. Bartholomew's Hospital. He there came under the influence of Sir William Lawrence, to whom he dedicated his book entitled *Diseases of the Eye and Ear consequent on- Inherited Syphilis*, published in 1863, consisting mainly of his reprinted articles in the *Ophthalmic Hospital Reports*.

It has already been mentioned in Chapter III. how much Lawrence did to increase the knowledge of venereal diseases of the eye by the careful collection and collation of notes of cases at the Ophthalmic Hospital. It was by the same careful collection and collation that Hutchinson was able to establish the connection of certain inflammatory eye affections with inherited syphilis, and he likewise found the most fruitful field for his investigations in the out-patient department at Moorfields. He was a most patient and elaborate note-taker, and, in apologising for the lengthy notes of some of his published cases, remarked:

" I must plead that they are the stones out of which the edifice is to be built, and that unless care be devoted to their preparation in the first instance, it will be useless to expend it on the subsequent elaboration."

Jonathan Hutchinson was a man intensely interested in the study of the natural history of disease in all its manifestations, and it may be added not only in the natural history of the disease, but of natural history generally. He was a great collector of facts, and had a remarkable flair for grouping them so as to draw new and unsuspected inferences.

He was not inaptly described as " the greatest general practitioner in Europe," and also as " the universal specialist." He was appointed assistant-surgeon to the London Hospital in 1859 and full surgeon in 1862; he was also surgeon at the Blackfriars Skin Hospital.

He attracted around him a large number of able assistants of whose devoted services he was able to make very material use. His biographer writes:

" His teaching was made impressive by ingenious arguments, apt illustrations, vivid metaphors, and quaint expressions, and was driven home by the simplicity and solemnity with which they were delivered."

On the retirement of Alfred Poland from the staff in 1861, it was decided that the surgical staff should be increased to eight in number by the appointment of two new assistant-surgeons. George Lawson and Jonathan Hutchinson were the only two candidates who came forward, and were both elected. Lawson, receiving a few more votes than Hutchinson, was appointed the senior of the two.

George Lawson, like Hulke, received his medical education at King's College Hospital. There was a remarkable parallelism between the careers of these two men. Both served as house surgeons under Sir William Ferguson. Both served as surgeons at the Crimea. Both became assistants to Bowman, and inspired by him combined ophthalmic surgery with general surgery. Both became general surgeons at the Middlesex Hospital, and ophthalmic surgeons at Moorfields.

Though their careers were so similar, temperamentally they were very different. Hulke was an austere, conscientious disciplinarian, who seemed to have had no youth. Lawson, on the other hand, was full of kindly sympathy for the weaknesses of mankind, and never seemed to grow old. This difference was no doubt to some extent attributable, as Lawson himself suggested, to Hulke having had no children, whilst Lawson had a large family of boys.

Hulke earned for himself the greater scientific reputation, but Lawson had by far the larger private practice. Hulke's articles in the early numbers of the *Reports* were numerous, some of them clinical records, but many of them dealing with histological and pathological investigations. Lawson's contributions were also numerous, and dealt mostly with injuries of the eye and sympathetic ophthalmitis. In 1867 he published his collected experience on these matters in a book entitled *Injuries of the Eye, Orbit, and Eyelids*. His attention had doubtless been specially attracted to such injuries during his service with the Army in connection with the Crimean War. Early in 1854, when war was threatening, Lawson joined the Army as an assistant-surgeon, and went in March of that year with the first batch of troops to Malta. He landed with the first troops in the Crimea, and was present at the battles of Alma and Inkerman. He was invalided home in July, 1855, with typhus fever, which he contracted from some mule drivers whom he was attending, and which left his circulation permanently impaired.

In Part III. of the *Reports*, Streatfield gave a description of his operation of grooving the fibro-cartilage of the eyelid in cases where its margin or the eyelashes turned inwards: an operation which is still frequently performed as originally described, or in a modified form.

In the last part of the first volume, which appeared in January, 1859, Dixon recorded a case in which he successfully removed a chip of steel from the vitreous chamber by grasping it with a pair of forceps. The case is of particular interest because it seems to have been the first in which an attempt to remove a foreign body from the interior of the eyeball with a powerful magnet was made, a line of practice which has since reached a high degree of usefulness. In Dixon's case, the effect of the magnet was only to drag the chip of steel into a less desirable position, so that a pair of forceps had to be used in order to effect its removal.

Amongst the numerous interesting articles in the second

volume of the *Reports* are some short contributions from the celebrated Glasgow ophthalmic surgeon, William Mackenzie, then in his fifty-ninth year, whose masterly *Practical Treatise on the Diseases of the Eye* had obtained world-wide reputation. After serving his apprenticeship and passing his qualifying examination in Glasgow, he visited the medical schools of Paris, Pavia, and Vienna; at the latter he studied ophthalmology under Professor Beer. In 1818 he settled for a time in practice in London, in Newman Street, Oxford Street, and delivered a systematic course of lectures on " Diseases and Operative Surgery of the Eye." Though we have no definite record of his attendance at the Eye Infirmary, then in Charterhouse Square there can be little doubt that his keen interest in ophthalmology must have taken him there. In 1820 he returned to Glasgow to fill the Anatomical Chair in the Andersonian University, and in 1824 he established the Glasgow Eye Infirmary. One of his articles in the *Reports* deals with glaucoma, and he was the first to point out its connection with the increased tension of the eye—an increase of tension which he endeavoured to relieve by paracentesis of the eye through the sclerotic or cornea.

To those familiar with the operation for removal of cataract, the fixing of the eyeball whilst making the incision, by grasping the conjunctiva with a pair of toothed forceps, seems such an obvious procedure that it is surprising that it should not have always been employed. We find, however, in the second volume of the *Reports*, an article by France advocating such fixation as a new departure. France was surgeon in charge of the ophthalmic department at Guy's Hospital. When Saunders first established a special institution for the treatment of eye diseases, and for many years afterwards, there were no such special departments at any of the London general hospitals. Guy's Hospital was the first of the general hospitals to establish an ophthalmic department, and by 1858 similar departments had been started at University College Hospital under Wharton Jones, and at St. Mary's Hospital under White Cooper. These two latter surgeons also contributed articles to the *Ophthalmic Hospital Reports*, which in its early days was not restricted to work carried on at Moorfields.

With the second volume of the journal the use of paper of a slightly yellow tint, instead of white, was commenced. Streatfield, the editor, explained that Charles Babbage, the mathematician, in printing his logarithmic tables, had experimented with specimens set up on paper of various shades and colours, and found that almost all those whom he consulted agreed with him in giving preference to the coloured papers. The particular tint, however, was not so unanimously fixed upon, though yellow appeared to have the preference. Several editions of Babbage's *Tables of Logarithms* were printed on the yellow and the white paper; the former were always in most demand. This slightly yellow tinted paper was apparently approved of by the contributors and readers of the journal, as it continued in use for several years.

In this same volume there commenced a series of articles on "Paralytic Affections of the Muscles of the Eye," by John Soelberg Wells, who in 1860 became one of Bowman's clinical assistants.

Soelberg Wells was a tall, handsome man, of splendid physique, and possessed of ample private means. He graduated in medicine at Edinburgh University in 1856, but much of his education and training, general and professional, was conducted by German teachers, for he was partly German by extraction. For two years previous to his commencing work at Moorfields he studied under Graefe in Berlin, and was for a time one of his assistants. In his lectures and in his clinique Graefe devoted much time and patience to teaching the diagnosis of paralytic affections of the eye muscles, and Wells' articles on the subject dealt with the rules he had learnt from Graefe, to the great accuracy and value of which he was able to testify.

In the third volume of the *Reports* commenced the publication of a " Periscope " of foreign ophthalmological literature; in this production Soelberg Wells' knowledge of German and of the Continental cliniques was of great service, and he translated for the use of English readers articles by Müller, Donders, and Graefe. By such means international scientific intimacy, which is so eminently desirable, was stimulated and promoted.

After the issue of the thirteenth number of the *Reports*, Streatfield resigned his editorship, and in April, 1861, what was termed a New Series was commenced, with the following prefatory remarks:

" The first number was issued October, 1857, and the publication, though not strictly quarterly, has subsequently appeared with regularity sufficient to complete two volumes.

" The later numbers, however, have assumed a very different appearance to those which were at first submitted to the profession, and it has therefore been deemed necessary to remodel the journal: at the same time, as it is the only periodical in England specially devoted to ophthalmic medicine and surgery, it is thought desirable to extend its limits, by admitting reviews and periscopes, and thus to make it more generally useful.

" It will be edited by members of the staff, and appear under the title *Ophthalmic Hospital Reports, and Journal of Ophthalmic Medicine and Surgery.*"

Apparently very heavy expenses had been incurred in former numbers for engravings and coloured lithographs, which made a change of management desirable, for it was noted:

" In future the amount of illustration will much depend on the support of the professional public, the medical officers of the Royal London Ophthalmic Hospital having led the way by devoting their fees, received from pupils, to the interests of the journal."

The art of perimetry or of taking the field of vision, which has now reached such a high degree of accuracy and importance, seems to have originated with von Graefe in 1856, and to have been first employed at Moorfields by Hulke in 1859. In the third volume of the *Reports* he described some cases, as he says, " to illustrate some forms of limitation of the field of vision."

Hulke's method of procedure was similar to Graefe's. He placed the patient before a large blackboard at a distance of 8 inches, covered one of his eyes, and made him fix a chalked dot in the centre of the board, on a level with his eyes, with the other. He then moved a white object over the board in various directions from its margins towards the centre and marked the places where it was first seen. A line connecting these marks gave the outline of the field of vision.

The obvious defect of using a flat surface, like a blackboard, was that the various parts of the retina were not situated at an equal distance from it. To Förster belongs the credit of having introduced an instrument in which the field was projected on a hollow sphere. His perimeter consisted of a metallic semicircle capable of rotation in various meridians, and on this general principle all other models since produced have been constructed. Förster's perimeter first came into use at Moorfields in 1870.

The rapid development of surgical procedures in ophthalmology eclipsed for a time at Moorfields the medical side. Dr. Robert Martin, who held the post of physician from 1856 to 1884, made but little use of the opportunities it afforded him. He did not have patients allotted to him or any fixed time of attendance, like his predecessor. In 1867 he suffered from a severe illness which seemed to threaten his mind, and necessitated his temporary retirement from all work; he, however, completely recovered, and no one was appointed in his place at Moorfields during his absence.

The discovery of the ophthalmoscope opened up a new

field for medical investigation, which was fully taken advantage of by that distinguished neurologist, Dr. Hughlings Jackson, who at the commencement of his career worked at Moorfields, first with Poland and afterwards with Jonathan Hutchinson. In a Presidential Address which he delivered at the Ophthalmological Society in 1889, he remarked:

" It was the luckiest thing in my early life that I began the scientific study of my profession at an Ophthalmic Hospital. Many years ago I had the good fortune to be Mr. Hutchinson's clinical assistant at Moorfields. I suppose it is to his example and teaching that I owe the beginning of the little scientific development I may have. At an Ophthalmic Hospital one has the opportunity of being well disciplined in exact observation. When a physician sees how carefully and precisely ophthalmic surgeons investigate the simplest case of ocular paralysis, he is getting a lesson in exactness, and will be less likely in his own department of practice to deal in such generalities as that a patient's fit ' had all the characters of an ordinary epileptic fit,' and more likely to take pains to describe the convulsion, the place of onset, the march and the range of the spasm."

Dr. Hughlings Jackson contributed many most valuable papers to the *Reports* dealing with ophthalmoscopic findings in connection with brain disease. He wrote, as he said in one of them, " as a physician and not as an ophthalmologist," having studied ophthalmic medicine merely as a help to the study of diseases of the nervous system. And, again, in another article he remarked:

" The physician is quite as much indebted to Helmholtz as the ophthalmologist. Defects of sight of all kinds occur so often in affections of the nervous system that it is not too much to say that to the student of these diseases a knowledge of amaurosis, both in the widest and loosest, and in the narrowest and most precise use of the word, is of more importance than a knowledge of any other class of symptoms."

He was never tired of impressing on physicians the value of the routine use of the ophthalmoscope. Thus he wrote in 1889:

" I urge young physicians to study eye diseases at an Ophthalmic Hospital or at an ophthalmic department of a General Hospital; this nowadays needs no urging on physicians especially interested in neurology."

In 1863 Dr. Argyll Robertson contributed a paper from Edinburgh to the *Reports*, " On the Effects of Calabar Bean on the Eye," in which he stated that the miotic action of this drug had been first discovered by Dr. Thomas R. Fraser. Besides describing its effects on the normal eye, he enumerates several affections in which he had found its use beneficial, but makes no mention of glaucoma. It was apparently not until 1876 that it became employed for the reduction of increased intraocular tension, Adolph Weber and Laquer describing its use for this purpose about the same time.

CHAPTER IX
GROWTH AND EXTENSION

WHEN the Eye Infirmary was first built in lower Moorfields in 1821 the district was an exceedingly quiet one; in front of it was a large open space, which had been the old Bethlehem Hospital burial-ground, but had not been used as such after the removal of that Hospital to the other side of the river in 1814.

In 1899, when the Eye Hospital was transferred to the City Road, the district had become one of the busiest and noisiest in the City of London. The cause of this change was the erection of the Broad Street and Liverpool Street Stations on the site of the old burial-ground, and on that of a large number of courts and alleys in its vicinity, which were cleared away for the purpose. Out of these terminal stations there poured forth every morning the various City workers, and back to them they streamed in the afternoons and evenings. The railway termini became the starting-points of various omnibuses, the roll of the wheels of which on stony streets and the clatter of the horses' hoofs kept up a continuous roar. The erection of the London and North-Western Railway's Goods Station, to the north of the Hospital on the opposite side of Eldon Street, added noises at night, as well as day, in the rattle and banging of milk-cans. To patients coming from country districts this continuous noise proved very disturbing and detrimental. In 1870 some mitigation of the trouble was obtained by the substitution of asphalt paving in the streets around the Hospital in place of cobble-stones.

The increased facilities which the railways and omnibuses afforded for approach to the Hospital tended largely to increase the number of patients coming to it for relief. In 1851 the new out-patients numbered 11,384, and in 1878 they had increased to 19,177. To provide accommodation for this increase, and for the larger number of patients requiring operative treatment, it became obvious that a new wing would have to be added on the south side of the Hospital. A lease for the land on which it was to be erected had, through the foresight of Dr. Farre, been obtained in 1823 for a period of seventy-seven years from the Corporation of London. On it a stables had been built and let off until such time as the Hospital found it necessary to take possession. When the new building was contemplated, an attempt was made to obtain a freehold of the site from the Bridge House Estate, but owing to the Hospital not being an incorporated body the negotiations fell through.

The original London terminus of the Great Eastern Railway, opened in 1839, was at Shoreditch. In 1863 a Bill was introduced into the House of Lords to give the Great Eastern Railway power to extend their line to Finsbury Circus, and to make a station there which would absorb all the surrounding houses and the recently erected London Institution. It was obvious that such an undertaking would seriously interfere with the amenities of the Hospital, and the Committee of Management drew up a petition against the Bill, pointing out how the work of the Hospital would be interfered with if it was passed. This petition they confided to Mr. Alfred Smee, who at that time resided in Finsbury Circus, to be forwarded to the Earl of Shaftesbury for presentation to the House of Lords.

The Bill was rejected and the Committee of the Hospital passed a vote of thanks to the Right Hon. the Earl of Shaftesbury for his important services in the matter.

Pending the final selection of sites by the different railways for their terminal stations, the Committee of the Hospital had to postpone their plans for enlargement, but ultimately, early in 1868, the long contemplated building was commenced; it did not, however, become ready for occupation until July, 1870; the total cost was £7,226, towards which Her Majesty the Queen graciously contributed £100.

The reform in hospital architecture which commenced after the Crimean War with the publication of Miss Nightingale's celebrated *Notes on Hospitals* was then still in its infancy. St. Thomas's Hospital, which was being erected on the Thames Embankment at the same time as the new wing at Moorfields, was the embodiment of her ideas; adequate cubic space, not only in the wards but also in the passages, being considered the most essential factor. It has been jokingly said that, at St. Thomas's, so large and lofty is the children's ward that it is difficult to find the children. Listerism, with its passion for aseptic cleanliness, rounded corners, and polished surfaces, had not then dawned.

The new wing at Moorfields was designed by Mr. Robert Brass, and consisted of three floors. The ground floor was devoted to out-patients. The first and second floor each contained three small six-bedded wards leading out of a long passage. Their arrangement was neither good for administration or for ventilation. The curious device was adopted of placing the fireplaces immediately beneath the windows, which necessitated an elbow-shaped bend in the chimneys. The consequence was that soot which collected in the bends caught fire, causing from time to time considerable consternation and excitement amongst the patients and resident staff.

In 1866 the staff of the Hospital consisted of four surgeons and four assistant-surgeons, but Critchett was desirous of having an assistant-surgeon to work with him on his days of attendance, and it was mainly at his instigation that it was decided to appoint a fifth assistant-surgeon. To this post John Couper, who for several years had acted as Critchett's clinical assistant, and who was an assistant-surgeon at the London Hospital, was unanimously elected.

In 1867 the President of the Hospital, Mr. William

Cotton, D.C.L., F.R.S., died, and the Governors obtained the consent of the distinguished banker, scientist, and statesman, Sir John Lubbock, F.R.S., M.P. (afterwards Lord Avebury), to take his place.

In that year yet another addition was made to the surgical staff by the election as assistant-surgeon of John Soelberg Wells, to whose early career and scientific attainments reference has already been made. By that time several of the assistant-surgeons, by acting as such for five years, had become eligible for promotion to surgeons; it was not, however, until the new wing was opened, which provided an additional thirty-six beds, that they were able to obtain the full advantages of such promotion.

The establishment of special ophthalmic departments at the several general hospitals in London caused the Governors of Moorfields some alarm as to the ultimate welfare of their own institution, or as Critchett picturesquely put it, " they feared that the heart of the parent would be sucked out for the benefit of their children, without any corresponding advantage to the public." It was for this reason that in 1864, at a meeting of the Governors, the following rule was passed:

" No surgeon of the Hospital shall hold an ophthalmic appointment in any other institution, and if any surgeon, at the time when he becomes such, holds any ophthalmic appointment, he shall resign the same within three months"

The first time this rule came into operation was when Streatfield and Hulke became surgeons. The rule only applied to surgeons, not to assistant-surgeons. Streatfield held the post of ophthalmic surgeon at University College Hospital, and Hulke that of ophthalmic surgeon at Middlesex Hospital. On their promotion at Moorfields, the Committee of Management requested them to resign their appointments as ophthalmic surgeons elsewhere. Hulke readily complied with the request, as he was still able to maintain his connection as a general surgeon with the Middlesex. Streatfield, however, who only practised as an ophthalmic surgeon, was very reluctant to resign his connection with University College. On the matter being discussed by the Medical Council, it was found that its members were divided in their opinions: some, like Critchett, feared rivalry from the newly developing ophthalmic departments at general hospitals; others welcomed their up-growth, and saw that they were essential parts of such institutions, both from the patients' and the students' point of view. They considered it desirable that those who enjoyed the exceptional experience afforded as surgeons at Moorfields should be encouraged to join them, and that, as has proved to be the case, their connection with them would induce students requiring extended ophthalmic training to come to Moorfields. With such division of opinion on the surgical staff the Committee did not at that time consider themselves able to advise any alteration in the rule, and Streatfield had to resign his appointment at University College Hospital.

When Couper and Soelberg Wells became eligible for promotion as surgeons in 1873, the matter again came under consideration; in the interval several members of the staff had altered their opinions, and the Medical Council unanimously recommended the abolition of the rule, stating that " it felt assured that the cultivation of intimate relation with General Hospitals through members of the staff is conducive to the interests of Moorfields." A special meeting of the Governors was then summoned, at which the rule was rescinded. Streatfield was fortunate enough to be reappointed to the post he had had to resign at University College.

James Dixon retired from the active staff of the Hospital in 1868, after having been connected with it for twenty-five years, and the senior surgeon for a period of twelve years. As such he had a seat on the Committee of Management, where he was a regular attendant and rendered valuable assistance. In 1870, owing to domestic bereavements, he gave up practice and lived in retirement, occupying himself with the study of English history and English literature. He published a small handbook, entitled *A Guide to the Practical Study of the Diseases of the Eye*, in which he said he aimed at supplying a useful guide to those commencing the study of eye diseases. That it fulfilled this purpose is shown by its having passed through three editions. The last, which appeared in 1866, was brought well up to date with the numerous developments which had taken place since it first made its appearance.

Dixon was particularly scathing on the dry and pedantic use of unnecessarily complicated names in the description of affections of the eye. Thus he writes:

" It requires a more intimate knowledge of Greek than one has a right to expect from every student of medicine to recognise in ' Iridoperiphakitis ' an inflamed iris and capsule, or at once to detect the operation for closing lacrymal fistula under such a disguise as that of ' Dacryocysto-syringokatlesis.' "

Though the world-wide reputation of Moorfields is mainly due to the skill and scientific attainments of the medical staff, its progress and prosperity have been to a large extent promoted by the services of the able and devoted workers who have in succession held the post of Chairman of the Committee of Management. Conspicuous among them for the interest they took in everything connected with the Institution were Mr. F. G. Sambrooke, who died in 1871, after having held the post for eleven years, and Mr. Philip Cazenove, who succeeded him.

The medical staff of a hospital are the distributors of its benefits, but in order that benefits may be distributed a collecting department is essential, and the work of raising funds for its maintenance falls upon the Committee of Management and the secretary.

Some individuals seem to have a special flair for begging successfully for funds for charitable purposes. The united efforts of Mr. Sambrooke, the Chairman at Moorfields, and of Mr. Mogford, its secretary, during the sixties, met with a most excellent response. In the early days of the Hospital funds were raised by means of festival dinners and special sermons; but during the sixties, without such aid, subscriptions flowed in both for the maintenance of the Institution and for its building fund. Mr. Mogford attributed his success in this matter entirely to his letters of appeal; but it must be remembered that it was a time of peace and considerable commercial prosperity, under which conditions philanthropic efforts stand the best chance of success. Excellent as Mr. Mogford was as a collector of funds, he had certain weaknesses which in 1872 necessitated his resignation, Mr. Robert J. Newstead being appointed to fill his place.

In Mr. Sambrooke the medical staff had a most sympathetic supporter in the promotion of the scientific side of ophthalmology. During his chairmanship most liberal grants of money were made towards the development and upkeep of the Museum and Library. Thus a grant of £72 was made in 1864 for the purchase of a collection of ophthalmoscopic drawings of the fundus of the eye, and when the new museum was completed in 1870 a grant of £235 was expended in book-cases and suitable fittings for the display of specimens.

Charles Bader, who continued to hold the post of curator of the Museum up to 1867, as the outcome of his experiences published a book entitled *The Natural and Morbid Changes in the Human Eye*. He was very dexterous in the mounting of museum specimens of the eye, but unfortunately the only two methods then known of preserving such specimens were by means of spirit or by the use of glycerine. The former caused them to shrink and rendered the transparent parts opaque, and the latter, though to some extent preserving their transparency, caused them to swell. The introduction of the glycerine jelly method of preserving museum specimens of eyes by Nettleship in 1871, and elaborated by Priestley Smith in 1883, was a great improvement; but even with this method considerable care and attention was necessary to prevent deterioration. It was not until the introduction of formaline as a hardening and preserving agent, by Professor Leber in 1894, that a really satisfactory medium for museum specimens was found—one which would retain indefinitely the relative degrees of transparency and colour of the different parts which they presented during life.

On the resignation of Bader of the post of curator, Bowater Vernon, who had been working as clinical assistant to Wordsworth, was appointed in his place with a salary of £50 per annum. The duties of the post were defined as follows:

" That he shall attend daily from 10 to 1, and on the evenings of the ophthalmoscopic demonstrations, and at such other times as may be necessary to put up and display the morbid specimens presented.

" That he be responsible for the due keeping, cataloguing, and giving out under regulations of the books and plates under his charge.

" That he shall prepare gradually a complete series of preparations illustrating the normal anatomy of the human eye and its appendages, and proceed as far as possible with a similar series illustrative of the comparative anatomy and pathology of the same.

" That he shall be required to report upon the microscopic appearances of all specimens requiring such examination, and to keep a register of such examinations, if possible, illustrated by drawings."

The evening ophthalmoscopic demonstrations above referred to had been started for the benefit of the students attending the Hospital in 1864, and were conducted in turn by the different members of the staff.

In the records of pathological specimens, published by Vernon in the *Reports* in 1868, is the description of what must have been one of the first cases of tubercle of the choroid which, having been seen ophthalmoscopically, was later examined microscopically. In 1871 Vernon, being appointed ophthalmic surgeon to St. Bartholomew's Hospital, resigned the post of curator of the Museum; he was succeeded by Edward Nettleship, who held it for two years in conjunction with that of clinical assistant to Jonathan Hutchinson. The extensive reports of the specimens committed to his care which Nettleship published in the *Hospital Reports* for those years show with what care and diligence he discharged the duties of the office. This, together with the stimulating influence of his chief, Jonathan Hutchinson, formed an excellent training for the important work which Nettleship did in connection with ophthalmology in later years.

In the middle of the nineteenth century a number of residential schools were established in London for the children of parents in receipt of Poor Law relief. Almost from their commencement outbreaks of ophthalmia became very prevalent in these schools. In 1870 Critchett was asked to visit and advise as to the ophthalmia in one of them at Anerley. He stated in his report that he

" found a large proportion of mild ophthalmia, which in most cases did not render the patients incapable of following the usual educational course, and he advised the establishment of a ward or separate school, where all such cases might be kept for an indefinite time until it was quite certain that they would not relapse, where they might be under such hygienic and medical treatment as seemed necessary, where their instruction and education should go on as if they were in the body of the school, and where, by prolonged isolation, they might be prevented from acting as sources of contagion to the healthy children in the school."

Action was taken in accordance with this advice in 1873, when 400 children who showed signs of ophthalmia at the Anerley School were isolated in an unoccupied workhouse

PLATE XVII.

EDWARD NETTLESHIP, F.R.S.

[To face p. 140

at Bow, which was kept going as a combined infirmary and school with an efficient staff of teachers and nurses for twelve months. Nettleship, having resigned his appointment as curator at Moorfields, acted as its resident superintendent. The experiment proved the soundness of Critchett's advice, but it became obvious that in some cases, more especially those of trachoma, isolation and treatment would have to be continued for more than a year. In 1889 a special isolation school was erected for children affected with ophthalmia in the Central District School at Hanwell, and placed under the charge of Sydney Stephenson. Here, again, the success of Critchett's policy was so marked, that in 1897 the Local Government Board instructed the Metropolitan Asylums Board to provide accommodation for children suffering from ophthalmia in all the Poor Law Schools of London. The result has been a steady and continuous diminution in the number of cases to be dealt with, and the practical extinction altogether in these schools of that most intractable of all forms of ophthalmia—trachoma.

The salary for the curator of the Museum, whilst Vernon and Nettleship held the office, seems to have been disproportionately small to the liberal grants made for the upkeep of the Museum itself. During his first year of office Nettleship's salary was only £50 per annum; at the end of that time, " in consideration of his very valuable and arduous services in the work of the Museum," it was raised to £75. When W. A. Brailey was appointed to the post in 1874 it was found necessary to increase the salary of it to £100, and in 1877 to £120. After increased accommodation was made in connection with the laboratory in 1879, courses of instruction in practical pathology of the eye were commenced by the curator.

In 1870 ophthalmic science sustained a heavy loss by the death of Albert von Graefe, its most zealous and successful cultivator, in his forty-third year. His last extensive article, dealing with " The Pathology and Treatment of Glaucoma," was translated and published in full in the *Ophthalmic Hospital Reports* at the beginning of 1871. Much as Graefe did to extend our knowledge of the conditions which lead to an increased hardness of the eyeball, the disasters to which such hardness gives rise, and the means by which they may be avoided, much was still left unexplained. Even now, in spite of the reams which have since been written, there is still much in connection with the subject requiring further elucidation. In 1878 a stimulus was given to research in this country in connection with glaucoma by the Royal College of Surgeons setting as the subject for the Jacksonian Prize Essay for that year, " Glaucoma: its Causes, Symptoms, Pathology, and Treatment." The prize was awarded to Priestley Smith, of Birmingham, and articles dealing with its causation were published in the *Hospital Reports* for 1881 by him, and by the curator of the Museum, W. A. Brailey. The following year Brailey resigned the curatorship on his being appointed assistant ophthalmic surgeon at Guy's Hospital. His successor was W. Jennings Milles, who had previously been house surgeon; he, however, only held the post for eighteen months, resigning it to go to Shanghai. He thus carried the practice and training of Moorfields to the Far East, as others had done to all parts of the British Empire, and to many of the leading cities in the United States of America.

In 1873 a Canadian, Frank Buller, was appointed house surgeon, and, returning subsequently to Montreal, became the pioneer of ophthalmic surgery in that colony. Incidentally, it is of interest to note that in doing so he forestalled another young Canadian named Osler (afterwards Sir William Osler, Bart.), who had come to Moorfields to study eye diseases with the same end in view, but, learning there of Buller's intentions, he abandoned the practice of ophthalmology for that of general medicine.

The length of time which those holding office at Moorfields retained their posts, and the reluctance with which

PLATE XVIII.

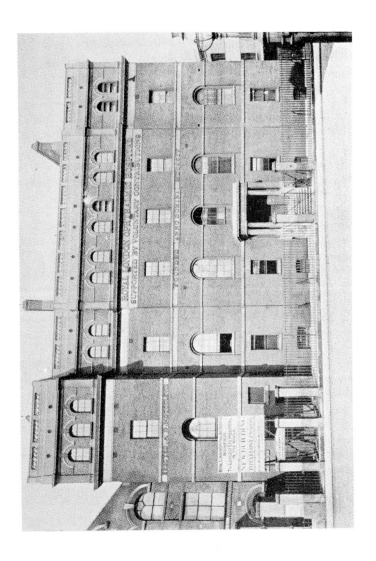

THE HOSPITAL AT MOORFIELDS AFTER THE ADDITION OF A NEW WING IN 1868, AND A NEW STORY IN 1875.

they resigned them, bears eloquent testimony to their interest in the work of the Institution. There was then no limit to the time that a house surgeon might retain his post, and some continued to do so for more than three years. In 1870 Miss Boycott, who had held the post of matron for twenty-one years, died at the Hospital. Miss Harnet succeeded her, but not being herself a trained nurse did little to raise the standard of nursing, which remained during her term of office in a very primitive condition.

As the number of new out-patients attending the Hospital continued to increase—from 19,177 in 1868 to 20,687 in 1875—it soon became evident that the newly erected wing did not supply all the in-patient accommodation that was required. In 1875 a plan was drawn up and adopted for the erection of another storey on the main building at a cost of £2,430. This was completed the following year, when the accommodation of the Hospital became increased to 45 beds for male patients, 51 for women and children, and 4 for occasional use.

Bowman and Critchett were nearly of the same age, Bowman being a little the senior. So much had they done to add to the fame and reputation of Moorfields that as they approached the age of sixty, when in accordance with the rules of the Hospital they would have to retire from the active staff and become consulting surgeons, the Committee of Management became anxious to find some way in which their services could be retained. Both Bowman and Critchett, like many of those who have come after them, felt very reluctant to sever their intimate association with the Hospital's work and welfare.

Bowman, in writing to the Chairman of the Committee in July, 1876, to inform him that the time for his retirement was nearly due, requested that the duties of a consulting surgeon might be defined, as so far nothing had been laid down concerning them. Critchett also wrote at the same time as follows:

" I believe that Mr. Bowman is about to send in his resignation, and I wish to reiterate my conviction that it will be a serious loss to the Hospital.   Every week I am a witness to the brilliant operations he performs, they are to me and to a crowded theatre a source of pleasure and profit; professors and students gather round him from far and near; the prestige of the Hospital and its value both in a scientific and benevolent aspect are enhanced by his presence, and by the admirable work that he does.   I am sure that if he had voluntarily left us, or if he had been snatched from us, every one attached to the Institution, whether lay or professional, would have felt that they had sustained an irreparable loss.   I would therefore suggest that some effort should be made to retain his services.   In appointing him to be consulting surgeon, it seems desirable that he should have a few beds placed at his disposal for the admission of cases that may be sent up to him or that any of his professional colleagues may wish to place under his care; also that he should be invited to continue his clinical teaching and if possible give some clinical lectures at stated times. This would be a great service to us all."

The Committee then, in accepting Bowman's resignation, passed the following resolution:

" That in acknowledgment of his high reputation and long services to this Institution the Committee request him to continue his clinical instructions, which they are sure will be as acceptable to the staff as to themselves, and for that purpose are pleased for the present to place five beds at his disposal."

In passing this resolution and forwarding it to Bowman the Committee acted without first consulting the Medical Council.   That body at once notified the Committee that it was unanimously of opinion that it was an infringement of the existing laws to assign beds thus to Bowman on his becoming consulting surgeon.   The Committee replied by requesting the Medical Council to consider regulations as to the duties of a consulting surgeon.   The Medical Council then proceeded to collect information as to the customs in force with reference to such officers at the principal Metropolitan Hospitals. It found that in all of them their duties were simply consultative, and that they attended only when specially summoned at the request of the officer in charge of the patient. The Medical Council then advised that a similar practice should be adhered to at Moorfields, and that arrangements might be made for the consulting surgeons to deliver clinical lectures. The Committee were very loath to withdraw the offer of the use of beds which they had made to Bowman, and had likewise extended to Critchett. The whole matter was discussed at the Annual Meeting of the Governors, with Sir John Lubbock, the President, in the Chair. In the end, Bowman and Critchett withdrew from all active participation in the work of the Hospital with somewhat embittered feelings.

Bowman died in 1892 at the age of seventy-six. In one of his obituary notices we read the following account of his doings after he left Moorfields:

" Fortunately, the opportunities for professional intercourse with Bowman did not cease with his retirement from Moorfields. Until some years later he held the leading place at all the chief meetings connected with our speciality. In 1880, when the British Medical Association held its Annual Meeting at Cambridge, Bowman was President of the ophthalmological section. Donders was present also. The Senate of the University conferred its honorary degree of LL.D. on both. In the following year Bowman presided over a still more important gathering in London—the ophthalmological section of the Seventh International Medical Congress. The fine nature of the man, his high ideals, simplicity, and modesty, are perhaps nowhere more clearly shown than in the inaugural address given by him on that occasion.

" The Ophthalmological Society of the United Kingdom was founded in 1880, and was fortunate in having Bowman as its president during its first three years—it was largely through his influence that the Society rose so rapidly into

strength and importance.   Its funds, moreover, were largely
increased by his generosity.   He was an ideal president:
speaking little, but always with purpose and effect, showing
interest in every communication and encouraging every
effort at good work.

"In the year 1883 the Council of the Ophthalmological
Society resolved to establish an annual lecture—the Bowman
lecture—'in recognition of Mr. Bowman's distinguished
scientific position in ophthalmology and other branches of
medicine, and in commemoration of his valuable services
to the Ophthalmological Society, of which he was the first
president.'   In the following year he was made a baronet
in recognition of his scientific attainments and professional
eminence.   A little later, the suggestion that his portrait
should be painted and presented to him was welcomed by
a large number of his friends, in this and other countries,
and the well-known portrait by Ouless, which was exhibited
in the Royal Academy in 1889, was the result.

"Not until he was seventy years of age did Sir William
Bowman relinquish active practice, and even for some years
longer he was still at times accessible to those who specially
desired his opinion and advice."

Critchett died in 1882 at the age of sixty-five.   After
retiring from Moorfields he was appointed ophthalmic
surgeon and lecturer on ophthalmology at the Middlesex
Hospital, an appointment which he held for four years.
It afforded him a few beds for needy patients, and his son
Anderson assisted him with the out-patients.   He soon
endeared himself to the students there, who valued his
teaching and the opportunity of watching his operative
dexterity.   For some years he suffered from enlarged
prostate, cystitis, and granular kidney, but it did not prevent
his attending to his practice with unabated vigour, and
performing his numerous social engagements with his
customary hospitality up to the time of his death.

Several candidates who had acted as clinical assistants
presented themselves for the appointments on the staff
rendered vacant by the retirement of Bowman and Critchett,
but all withdrew in favour of Waren Tay and James Adams,

both of whom were assistant general surgeons at the London Hospital.

After the publication of Donders' great work in English *On the Anomalies of Accommodation and Refraction of the Eye*, by the New Sydenham Society in 1864, and Soelberg Wells' smaller book, which embodied Donders' teaching, *On Long, Short, and Weak Sight*, sight-testing and the correction of errors of refraction with glasses grew progressively in importance.

The prescription of lotions or ointments for the eyes took far less time than the estimation of refractive errors and the prescription of glasses, and with the increase of sight-testing the length of time occupied in dealing with out-patients became considerably prolonged. At first it was only the correction of the grosser errors of refraction which received attention, but as the methods for their estimation improved, and the importance of even small errors became recognised, the amount of refractive work steadily increased.

The length of time many out-patients had to wait before they received attention became a source of anxiety, extending over many years, not only to the Committee of Management, but also to the surgical staff. The surgeons' time was fully occupied with the investigation of diseased conditions and with operating; they had to depend mainly for the carrying out of this refraction work on the devotion and goodwill of their clinical assistants, who, being purely voluntary workers, could not always be relied upon to stay for an indefinite time.

Many measures were tried to overcome the difficulty. Hulke, who had a passion for punctuality, was never tired of urging the value of his special virtue on all concerned. Though a painfully punctual individual on a medical staff may at times be very trying to his colleagues and assistants, it is no doubt that he is a valuable asset to the institution with which he is connected. Everybody knew at Moor-

fields that on Hulke's days of attendance they had to be early
risers, with the result that the work was finished more
expeditiously.

Much trouble in connection with the refraction work of
the Hospital would probably have been avoided if the plan
which has recently been adopted, of paying an honorarium
to one clinical assistant for each surgeon, had been sooner
resorted to. It was originally recommended by the Medical
Council in 1877, but the Committee could not for a long
time see its way to increase so considerably the Hospital's
annual expenditure.

Jonathan Hutchinson, as has already been mentioned, was
a man who took the widest interest in all diseased conditions; the one subject which did not specially attract him
was refraction work. As the amount and importance of it
increased, and after he became deprived of the zealous help
of his two able assistants, Tay and Nettleship, he felt he
could no longer conscientiously carry out all the duties of
his post, and in 1878 resigned his appointment on the staff.

No man at Moorfields ever made more thorough and
effectual use of the clinical work which it placed at his
disposal than Jonathan Hutchinson. For several years he,
together with Wordsworth, edited the *Hospital Reports*,
and it was during that time that they were conducted
with the highest degree of efficiency and regularity. The
" Periscope " in those years, which was mainly the work
of Waren Tay, formed an excellent and very complete
review of foreign ophthalmic literature. Hutchinson's own
articles were numerous, containing groups of well-recorded
cases, designed to illustrate new and interesting observations.

In the November number of the *Reports* for 1871 he
published " Statistical Details of Four Years' Experience in
Respect to the Form of Amaurosis supposed to be due to
Tobacco." It was his third article on the subject; the first,
in which he suggested a connection between excessive

smoking and affections of the optic nerve, having appeared in 1864. His attention became attracted by the almost exclusive occurrence of what was then called " idiopathic symmetrical amaurosis " in the male sex. He considered all the possible causes which might account for such a prevalence in one sex only, and found the tobacco hypothesis the most probable. His researches showed that there was little evidence of any other affection of the nervous system in these cases, and that all of them were excessive smokers, most of them having used shag tobacco. Having watched them for some time, he discovered that when the disuse of tobacco was real and complete vision generally improved.

The less frequent issue of the *Reports* after Hutchinson's departure, and the abandonment of the " Periscope," was due to two things—the establishment of the Ophthalmological Society in 1881, and the commencement of the *Ophthalmic Review* in 1882.

The unexpected vacancy on the staff caused by Hutchinson's resignation was filled by the election of John Tweedy, who was a clinical assistant to Streatfield, and held the post of assistant ophthalmic surgeon at University College Hospital.

In 1879 Philip Cazenove resigned the post of Chairman of the Committee of Management which he had held for eight years, and in doing so presented the Hospital with a gift of £1,000. Charles Gordon, whose name was, and is still, well known in connection with gin, was appointed to succeed him.

The Hospital suffered a severe loss by the death of Soelberg Wells in December, 1879; his health had been failing for some time, and he had been granted repeated periods of leave from his work at the Hospital on account of it. His *Treatise on the Diseases of the Eye*, first published in 1869, ran through three editions, and was translated into German and French. It was for a long time the standard textbook on ophthalmology, having the supreme virtue of combining the best teaching and practice of continental writers on the subject with those of our own country, an undertaking for which Soelberg Wells was particularly well fitted, owing to his familiarity with the continental clinics and his linguistic abilities.

Robert Lyell, who had worked as Hulke's clinical assistant and who was an assistant general surgeon at the Middlesex Hospital, was elected in Wells' place. He was a man who, as a student, had had a brilliant career and had obtained the highest qualifications and distinctions. With his appointments at the Middlesex and Moorfields, the way seemed open to him for a successful and prosperous future. Unfortunately, in the summer holiday of 1882, he contracted pneumonia, and the opening session at the Middlesex Hospital Medical School in October, at which he was to have delivered the Introductory Address, was saddened by the news of his death.

For the vacancy created by Lyell's death several candidates presented themselves, but ultimately withdrew their applications in favour of Nettleship, who already held the post of ophthalmic surgeon at St. Thomas's Hospital. This was the last appointment on the staff at Moorfields which was created by a vote of the Governors. In 1883 the Medical Council informed the Committee of Management that in its opinion "the present mode of election of the honorary medical officers did not secure the best interests of the Hospital." A joint conference was held at which it was decided to recommend that in future the election of honorary officers should be invested in a committee, and that this election committee should consist of the Board of Management, together with six honorary medical officers, the quorum to consist of seven; and that canvassing should be prohibited on the part of any candidate under pain of disqualification. These recommendations were agreed to at a meeting of the Governors, and in this way all subsequent

PLATE XIX.

WAREN TAY.

[To face p. 151

elections have been conducted. At the same time it was also agreed that the Fellowship of the Royal College of Surgeons of England should be the only requisite necessary for eligibility as a candidate for a post on the surgical staff.

Manners and characteristics, besides being inherited by children from parents, are also often acquired by pupils from teachers. The latter most frequently occurs where the teacher possesses a strong and impressive personality, and the taught are earnest and devout. This transmission of traits is not uncommonly met with in the medical profession, where some dominating member of a hospital staff impresses his individuality on those who work under him. A conspicuous example of this occurred at Moorfields, where Waren Tay and Edward Nettleship, who worked as clinical assistants to Jonathan Hutchinson, acquired, probably quite unconsciously, not only his mannerisms, but even his method of speech. Tay, like Hutchinson, became skilled in the practice of several different branches of his profession; like him, he became a general surgeon at the London Hospital, a specialist in skin diseases at the Blackfriars' Hospital and in eye diseases at Moorfields. It has already been mentioned how Hutchinson worked under Sir William Lawrence, and acquired from him the habit of collecting and collating the notes of clinical cases; in this most valuable method of advancing our knowledge of the natural history of disease Hutchinson found a most able disciple in Edward Nettleship, who, in the excellent field for its employment which Moorfields Hospital afforded him, made the most extensive use of it, more especially in tracing out the hereditary transmission of diseases and deformities.

CHAPTER X

ANTISEPTICS, BACTERIOLOGY, AND LOCAL ANÆSTHESIA

JOSEPH LISTER's first paper on his method of preventing the access to wounds of germs which cause putrefaction appeared in the *Lancet* in 1867. It was not, however, until several years later that London surgeons began to adopt his methods, and it was not until the teaching and training of bacteriological laboratories exerted their influence that the practice of Listerian principles became generally and efficiently carried out.

Wounds of the eye, due to the protective influence afforded by the eyelids, and to their continuous irrigation with tears, which normally possess bactericidal powers, were less liable to septic infection than those in other parts of the body. Hence, prior to the introduction of antiseptic methods, the operations of ophthalmic surgery were less frequently complicated by septic troubles than those of general surgery.

Where the tear duct became obstructed and discharge from the tear sac regurgitated into the eye, and where contaminated instruments were introduced into the interior of the eyeball, wounds became infected and disastrous consequences ensued. The danger of operating for cataract when there was obstruction to the tear duct was soon recognised, and it became a routine practice to investigate the condition of the tear passages before embarking on such operations. It was not until some time after the introduction of antiseptic surgery that the sterilisation of the instruments used in ophthalmic operations became general.

In the third edition of Soelberg Wells' *Treatise on Eye*

Diseases, published in 1873, which may certainly be taken as picturing the high-water mark of ophthalmic practice at that date, no mention is made of the use of any antiseptic precautions in connection with operations on the eye.

The after-treatment of eyes operated on for extraction of cataract at Moorfields in 1876 is described by A. S. Morton, who was then house surgeon, as follows:

" As soon as the operation was completed the lids of each eye were fastened by a very narrow vertical strip of plaster, to prevent involuntary opening of the eye during recovery from the anæsthetic, then a piece of lint, on which was placed a layer of cotton-wool for each eye, and over all a bandage. The eyes were dressed each morning and evening after the operation, being gently bathed with tepid water and the lids oiled with a soft brush to prevent the dressing sticking to them. The patients were kept in bed till the third day, and the lids never opened till the fourth or fifth day after the operation, unless there were indications of mischief. About the end of a week they were handed over to the nurse to dress, and in about nine or ten days were allowed to have their eyes open, but very carefully shaded."

Confinement in a dark room was for a long time regarded as an essential part of the treatment of certain eye diseases. Some elderly people still retain vivid recollections of having to submit to this unpleasant form of treatment for some inflammatory eye affection in their youth. The admission of light to the eye during the first few days after an operation for cataract was believed to excite inflammation, and elaborate precautions were taken to avoid it.

The cataract wards at Moorfields were darkened with double blinds, and when the dressings on the eyes were being changed, a nurse stood at the end of the bed holding a candle which she cautiously shaded with her hand to prevent any of its rays falling on the patient's eyes. Some of the senior members of the staff received rather a shock when a venturesome house surgeon, mindful of Florence Nightingale's dictum that " a dark room is always a dirty room," had the blinds in the cataract wards drawn up, letting the sun's blessed rays stream in, whilst the patient's eyes were tied up or shaded with dark glasses.

The practice with regard to the instruments in the pre-antiseptic days was for the nurse to wash them when used in ordinary tap-water, after which they were stored in their velvet-lined cases. From these they were transferred without further preparation, and handed to the surgeon for the next operation on a tray lined with green baize.

Out-patients and inpatients were operated on in the same theatre, the former coming to it just as they presented themselves at the Hospital, without any change of clothing. The surgeons themselves made no change in their costume when operating, and the nurses wore no regular uniform.

The former violent " antiphlogistic " treatment of extensive bleeding, sweating, vomiting, and purging, for inflammatory affections of the eyes, had in the seventies been given up, chief reliance being then placed on the use of belladonna and poppy-head fomentations, " astringents," and the application of leeches, blisters, and setons to the temples.

The year 1872 was an unusually disastrous one at Moorfields as regards operations for the removal of cataract, as many as 20 per cent. having resulted in failure. A joint meeting of the Committee and the medical staff was held to consider the matter, and the disasters were attributed to the presence in the Hospital at the time of a large number of infectious cases, changes in the nursing staff, and the absence of the house surgeon on a holiday. Measures to improve the ventilation of the wards were taken, an assistant house surgeon was appointed, and a long standing request of the Medical Council for the appointment of a special night nurse was at last acceded to.

At the International Congress of Medicine held in London in 1881, a discussion took place at the ophthalmological section on the employment of antiseptics in ophthalmic surgery. Antiseptic surgery at that time consisted in the use of carbolic acid in the form of a spray, as a lotion, and in the dressings. Professor Horner of Zurich, who opened the discussion, quoted his statistics of cataract operations from 1867 to 1881 to show that by the use of antiseptics there had been a decrease in the number of cases of suppuration from 6·6 to 1·1 per cent. Some speakers thought the good obtained from the use of carbolic acid was counterbalanced by its irritating properties. Bowman, who presided over the section, in his Inaugural Address, made the following wise remarks which may be taken as foreshadowing the adoption of aseptic as opposed to antiseptic measures:

" I presume that no one nowadays will question the evils we are so familiar with in our practice, and which have so often marred the intention of well-devised operations skilfully performed, but where, as we hear it said, Nature has failed to do her part, to second the effort of the surgeon by a process of repair. The study of the causes of such failures and of the means of obviating them, constitutes far the most brilliant page of modern surgery; and in other sections of this Congress, while the name of Lister will be applauded, the wide questions he has raised, and in raising has so often cleared up, will receive the full consideration they call for.

" In the case of the organ of sight, specially constituted, and in some respects screened from injury as it unquestionably is, there are reasons why the application of precautionary antiseptic measures, though the principle of them must still assert itself, should take a somewhat special form. Owing to the local structural conditions they may apparently be often more simple, though the possible need of the more elaborate of them should never be allowed to fall out of view.

" The tears are a secretion as pure from extraneous particles as is the filtered air in the recesses of the lungs. They are poured out under cover, in the right place, in quantity suitable to the need; while the lids diffuse them over the conjunctival surface ere they escape to their proper channels. Their useful and multiple office is performed in a way so simple and so perfect, that no art, however skilful, could pretend to equal it. We should ponder well the deep marvels of adaptation of means to ends, and take heed that we do not hinder exquisite Nature by meddlesome or needless interference, by the *nimia diligentia Chirurgorum*, but only lend it tender and judicious help by our dressings and our methods. We should always still be able to apply the words of our great poet, ' The Art itself is Nature.' "

In 1876 A. S. Morton, the house surgeon at Moorfields, recorded that out of 146 cases of extraction of cataract 5·47 per cent. had suppurated, and that 12·3 per cent. had suffered from severe iritis. In an analysis of the results of cataract extraction at Moorfields for five years, from 1889 to 1893, the house surgeon, C. D. Marshall, records the number in which suppuration occurred as 1·69 per cent. The preparation and after-treatment of patients undergoing this operation during those years he describes as follows:

" I shall here only mention the special points connected with the eye, the general examination and preparation of the patient being precisely the same as that adopted previous to the performance of any surgical operation. The lids and parts around the eye are carefully washed with soap and hot water over-night, and a pad which has been wrung out in a $\frac{1}{4000}$ solution of the perchloride of mercury is applied. On removing this the next morning one is able to obtain a good idea as to the state of the conjunctiva; if the lids be gummed together, the operation is deferred until a more satisfactory state of things is obtained. If, however, there is nothing to contraindicate the performance of the operation the eye is anæsthetised with a 2 per cent. solution of freshly prepared cocaine and the conjunctival sac is washed out with a good stream of either warm boracic or perchloride lotion. The instruments are boiled before being used and kept in carbolic acid lotion 1 to 40.

" After the operation both eyes are as a rule closed for a day or two, and tied up with pads of Gamgee tissue made of the double cyanide wool. The operated eye is kept bandaged for about a week, and after that dark goggles are worn."

PLATE XX.

JOHN COUPER.

[To face p. 157

John Couper, who was a general surgeon at the London Hospital as well as an ophthalmic surgeon at Moorfields, was one of the earliest and most enthusiastic pioneers of antiseptic surgery, practising it consistently before Lister came to London. At Moorfields he was one of the first to welcome its application to ophthalmic surgery.

In the following appreciation, written by Sir John Tweedy, we have recorded a most faithful and striking word-picture of John Couper's characteristics:

" When I first knew John Couper he was assistant-surgeon to the London Hospital and assistant-surgeon to the Royal London Ophthalmic Hospital, Moorfields. With his work as a general surgeon I was but slightly acquainted, but I do know that he was one of the first and most ardent of the disciples of the Listerian doctrine, and practised the Listerian method with patient confidence. It was my happy privilege to have as colleagues at Moorfields George Lawson and John Couper, and to work side by side with them for many years. Lawson was one of the best ophthalmic *surgeons* I have ever known. Couper's gifts were of a different order. Although a good surgeon and a skilled operator, his qualities were those of an *ophthalmic physician*. *Facile princeps* among the ophthalmoscopists of the day, he was one of the first in this country seriously and scientifically to study problems of the errors of refraction, and especially of astigmatism. His diagnostic skill and his careful method of investigation attracted a body of thoughtful pupils, not a few of whom afterwards attained a notable distinction. Couper's was a charming personality; he was gentle, courteous, conciliatory, but strong in opinion and tenacious of principle. His mental temperament was essentially sceptical. Not unbelief, not mis-belief, but hardness of belief was his intellectual attitude to all surgical and scientific questions. He did not believe easily or lightly, but only when convinced by the force of reason and by the potency of well observed facts. His scepticism may not have been an unmixed benefit as a teacher to beginners, but it was a real advantage at a Hospital like Moorfields, where many of the pupils, assistants, and visitors were actual or potent experts. His hardness of belief often provoked keen but friendly controversy, sharp but generous differences of opinion, which rarely failed to elucidate truth, and open up fresh avenues of knowledge. No man was ever the worse for a difference of opinion with Couper, and most of us were often much the better. Thought was stimulated, reasons were clarified, opinions modified and amended, or maybe strengthened and confirmed; and, above all, a valuable lesson was learnt in mutual respect and tolerance. Couper was indeed a lovable man, a true friend, a staunch and loyal colleague. To have known him, and to have been so long associated with him, is an abiding satisfaction, and the recollection of a friendship unclouded throughout many years is a precious possession."

John Couper was not only a pioneer in the use of anti-septics in ophthalmic surgery, but also in the accurate correction of even small errors of refraction with glasses. He was most emphatic and uncompromising in advising his patients to wear their glasses constantly. A young lady with a very pretty face, who felt very loath to detract from its charms by wearing glasses, asked pitifully: " Please, Mr. Couper, how long shall I have to wear these glasses ?" Couper replied by asking her her age, which was eighteen. " Well," said Couper, " the average age of woman is three score years and ten; eighteen from that makes how long ?"

Couper made use of his ophthalmoscope not only to explore the fundus of the eye, but also as an optometer for the estimation of refractive errors. He commenced to do so before the practice of " retinoscopy " came into use, and having acquired considerable skill in the method, continued to employ it in preference to the easier one. To render the ophthalmoscope as serviceable as possible as an optometer, he introduced several modifications in it. He found it most desirable to have only one lens to look through behind the sight hole in the mirror at a time, and to be able to bring the eye of the observer as near as possible to that of the one being examined. For these purposes he substituted a chain of lenses in place of the usual disc, and, as he considered it necessary to have as many separate lenses available as are contained in an ordinary trial case, the handle of his ophthalmoscope in which the lenses circulated became of considerable length. So long, indeed, was it that Couper had to arrange with his tailor for the construction of a special coat pocket in which he could carry it.

The method of estimating errors of refraction of the eye by what is now known as " retinoscopy " was first introduced as a systematic method by Cuignet in 1874, under the inappropriate name of " keratoscopy." Bowman had, however, ten years previously called attention to the possibility of diagnosing regular astigmatism by using the mirror of the ophthalmoscope to reflect light into the eye, much in the same way as for detecting slight degrees of conical cornea.

An article advocating the use of Cuignet's method, by Litton Forbes, appeared in the *Ophthalmic Hospital Reports* in 1880, and another, descriptive of its optical basis, by W. Charnley, in 1882.

In 1883 John Cawood Wordsworth, having reached the age of sixty, retired from the active staff after thirty-one years of service, and died three years later from angina pectoris. He was described as an admirable example of the genuine " dignity and reputation of the profession," and as " unobtrusive almost to a fault." Though, together with Hutchinson, he was for several years editor of the *Hospital Reports*, he contributed but little himself to the literature of ophthalmology.

He resided and commenced to practise in Finsbury Square; for some time his private patients were but few and far between. He employed a page boy who was instructed to fetch him from the Hospital if any patient should happen to come whilst he was engaged there. One day the boy came to the Hospital in hot haste to announce the arrival of a patient. " Will he wait until I get round ?" Wordsworth asked the boy. " I am quite sure he will," replied the boy, " for I have locked him in." Wordsworth then explained to the house surgeon and his assistants how they must carry on the work for a time as he had been called away to see a private patient; they helped him on with his coat, and away he went with the boy. To their great surprise he returned after only a few minutes. Noting the surprised look in their faces, he sadly explained that it was only the tax collector.

Marcus Gunn, who had previously been the house surgeon, was appointed to succeed Wordsworth; he was the first officer who had so served the Hospital to become elected as a member of its honorary staff. He had been a particularly able and energetic house surgeon, having instituted a new system of note-taking for the in-patients, which has proved so satisfactory that it is still in use at the present time. His intimate acquaintance with the nursing and domestic arrangements of the Hospital proved of considerable value in the reforms and general upheaval which took place shortly after he was appointed. Previous to his becoming house surgeon, he had studied ophthalmology in Vienna under Jaeger; so impressed was he with the systematic courses of instruction carried on at that school, that on his appointment as assistant-surgeon he at once set to work to institute more regular and systematic teaching at Moorfields. He himself conducted regular classes in ophthalmoscopic examination at stated intervals, which became so popular that the list of students which could be taken at any one class was always filled up some time in advance.

Early in 1884 Dr. Martin resigned the post of physician, and Dr. Stephen Mackenzie (afterwards Sir Stephen Mackenzie), a physician at the London Hospital, was appointed in his place. He resided at that time in Finsbury Square, and it was easy, therefore, for him to attend at the Hospital when requested to do so either by a member of the surgical staff or the house surgeon. He took a keen

PLATE XXI.

R. MARCUS GUNN.

[To face p. 160

interest in medical ophthalmology, and contributed several communications on the subject to the Ophthalmological Society, of which he was one of the first secretaries.

During a large part of the nineteenth century the district of Finsbury was a fashionable residential medical quarter of London; Finsbury Square, Finsbury Pavement, Finsbury Circus, Broad Street, and St. Helen's Place, at one time swarmed with physicians and surgeons. The City and its adjacent districts were then largely inhabited by prosperous business folk and their families; as these migrated westwards, the doctors naturally followed suit. Many of the younger members of the staffs of St. Bartholomew's, Guy's, and the London Hospital lingered on so as to be within easy distance of those Institutions. It gradually became the custom for those residing around Moorfields Hospital, who were interested in ophthalmology, to foregather there in the house surgeon's room on certain evenings in the week to discuss cases and other matters of mutual interest. So far back as 1866 Jonathan Hutchinson records in the *Ophthalmic Hospital Reports* how he read a paper at the " Moorfields Club." It was at one of such informal meetings that early in 1880 a circular was drawn up suggesting the formation of an Ophthalmological Society. This was sent to the leading ophthalmic surgeons in the three divisions of the United Kingdom, and met with a cordial response. In June of that year the first meeting of " The Ophthalmological Society of the United Kingdom " was held, at which William Bowman, who had been appointed President, delivered an Inaugural Address.

Pasteur's researches on fermentation and putrefaction, and Lister's application of them to the treatment of wounds, raised the study of bacteriology to the dignity of a science.

Improvements in the microscope by the introduction of high power oil-immersion lenses made it possible to study the morphology of micro-organisms, and the introduction

by Koch of improved methods for obtaining pure culti-
vations of them paved the way to the investigation of their
life-history and bio-chemical reactions.

During the eighth decade of the nineteenth century the
connection of several different micro-organisms with diseases
of the eye was discovered, which aided in the study of their
natural history and treatment.

In 1884 incubators and other bacteriological apparatus
were installed in the pathological laboratory at Moorfields
to allow of these new methods of investigation being carried
out.

In 1882 Koch demonstrated that a specific organism
could be separated from tuberculous tissue and cultivated
outside the body, which would reproduce tuberculosis when
inoculated. A new test was thus supplied for the recognition of tuberculous lesions, and some affections of the eye,
of which the real nature up to that time had been doubtful,
were by its means proved to be tubercular. J. B. Lawford,
who, on the resignation of Jennings Milles, had become
curator of the Museum, was among the first to detect Koch's
bacillus in the tissues of the eye.

In 1890 Koch introduced his original form of tuberculin
treatment, which, before its effects had been adequately
investigated, raised the greatest expectations, and caused
a rush to Berlin of consumptives from all parts of the world.
This treatment was tested in January, 1891, on a patient
at Moorfields, under Waren Tay, with tubercular nodules
in the iris at the margin of the pupil. So situated it was
possible to watch the effects of the treatment on them with
the greatest precision. The nodules, which were at first
separate, gradually increased in size and became confluent,
ultimately invading neighbouring parts and necessitating the
removal of the eye. Besides demonstrating the failure of
the treatment, this case was of interest, because the administration of an injection of the tuberculin after the eye
was removed produced a general reaction, thus showing the

PLATE XXII

JAMES E. ADAMS.

From a painting by a patient upon whom he had performed the operation of extraction of cataract.

[To face p. 163

presence of some other focus of tuberculosis which had not been detected, and from which most probably the eye had become secondarily affected.

The employment of bacteriological investigation in connection with the discharge from eyes affected with ophthalmia resulted in the discovery of two new forms of bacilli—the Koch-Weeks bacillus in 1887, and the Morax-Axenfeld diplo-bacillus in 1896—each receiving a dual name due to their independent and almost simultaneous recognition by two different workers.

The recognition of these and other micro-organisms which had been discovered in connection with other affections (such as the gonococci, Klebs-Löffler bacilli, pneumococci, streptococci, and staphylococci), as the specific agents in the causation of the different forms of ophthalmia, led to a new means of classifying them, the previous classifications being based on the clinical appearances alone.

The rapid advance in bacteriology, and the introduction of vaccine treatment arising out of it, tended to make its study and practice more and more a special branch of medicine. In 1907, after the Hospital had been removed to the City Road, it was found necessary to erect a special laboratory for its development and to appoint a special officer to take charge of it.

The premature decease of several members of the surgical staff just as they had attained the acme of a successful career has already been referred to; the cruellest fate of all was that which befell James Adams, who, whilst engaged in restoring and saving the sight of others, was doomed to watch the gradual failure of his own to complete and irremediable blindness. This, too, whilst he was in the hey-day of life, a successful general surgeon at the London Hospital and ophthalmic surgeon at Moorfields. A man full of the joy of life, deservedly popular with his colleagues and students, he combined scientific with sporting interests, and was able to snatch a day here and there from his arduous duties to follow the hounds.

A complete rest having failed to prove of any benefit to his gradually increasing darkness, he, in the latter part of 1884, found it necessary to resign all his appointments. William Lang, who had for some time worked with him as clinical assistant, and who held the appointment of ophthalmic surgeon at the Middlesex Hospital, was elected as his successor at Moorfields.

Cocaine is derived from the leaves of a plant, *Erythroxylon coca*, which grows in Peru and Bolivia. It was originally named " khoka," meaning " the tree of trees." Joseph de Jussieu first sent a specimen of the plant to Europe in 1750. The practice of chewing its leaves as a means of appeasing hunger and thirst, and relieving fatigue, had for long been a custom among the natives of South America. The famous long-distance walker, Weston, employed them in this way when, in the seventies, he trudged round and round the Agricultural Hall in his efforts to cover the longest possible distance in the shortest possible time. In 1872 Dr. Hughes Bennett of Edinburgh showed that cocaine, when applied to a mucous membrane, produced anæsthesia, but no use was made of it in practice.

It was Karl Koller of Vienna, in 1884, who first made applications of it to the eye, which resulted in its employment in ophthalmic surgery. Koller's original article, describing the physiological effects of the drug on the eye, was so complete that there was but little left to be added. A description of it was given at the meeting of the Heidelberg Ophthalmological Society in 1884, and a solution of the drug was brought straight from there to Moorfields in the latter part of September of that year. The first operation performed under its influence in this country was a tattooing of the cornea by Marcus Gunn. Its employment soon became general in all operations on the eye in which there was not much congestion, and in which the tension of the globe was not increased. The supply at first was so small and the demand so great that its price rapidly rose to a guinea a grain.

The substitution of local for general anæsthesia in cataract operations aided materially in their safety and success. The dreaded effects on the eye of vomiting and reaching on the recovery from the administration of ether or chloroform were avoided, and the aid of the patient in turning the eye in any direction did away with the necessity of dragging it into suitable positions, which was frequently requisite when the patient was unconscious. The immediate result was a considerable decrease in the number of cases in which the vitreous humour escaped, and the possibility of greater precision in the adjustment of parts after the removal of the cataract.

At first nothing was known of its toxic effects, and the small amount absorbed when dropped into the eye did not give rise to them. It was only when attempts were made to anæsthetise large areas of the skin by subcutaneous injection that they became manifest.

In 1884 the surgical staff had become so dissatisfied with the system of nursing at the Hospital, and with the standard of the nurses employed, that they requested a conference with the Committee of Management on the matter. At this conference it was agreed that no satisfactory improvement could be effected without having at the head of the establishment a lady who had herself been efficiently trained as a nurse. Miss Harnet, who then held the post of matron, was advised to tender her resignation. This she did, a pension being granted her. The new matron, selected from a number of candidates for the post, was Mrs. Peel, who had been trained at the London Hospital, where she had also held the post of sister: later she had been matron at the Newcastle Infirmary.

Shortly after her appointment, the head nurse was detected receiving money from a patient; this being her second offence of the sort she was at once dismissed. After her departure it was discovered to have been a common form of corruption, notwithstanding the warning notices concerning it posted about the Hospital. The forced resignation of the former matron and the summary dismissal of the head nurse caused consternation amongst the other members of the nursing staff, who combined together to make things unpleasant for the new matron. She received, however, the support of the medical staff and the Committee of Management, and ultimately a complete change of the nursing staff was effected, fully trained nurses being engaged to fill all the most important posts.

In April, 1885, occurred the sudden and unexpected death of Streatfield, who was at that time the senior surgeon. As has already been mentioned, he was a most dexterous operator, and also possessed of considerable ingenuity, which manifested itself sometimes in peculiar ways. A few years before his death he had had constructed a gigantic model of an eye, on which he could demonstrate to students mechanically the various stages of operative procedures. As he truly pointed out, in operations on the eye, the smallness of the organ and of the parts dealt with renders it impossible for any, except those in close proximity to the operator, to see clearly what is taking place. He, therefore, devised this model, constructed with all its dimensions ten times the size of the normal eye. The eyelids and sclerotic were of white felt spread over wire, the cornea of glass, the iris of indiarubber, the lens of xylonite, and the external muscles of the eye of linen. Models of the instruments employed were of wood, also ten times their actual size, except as regards their handles, which to allow of the manipulation of such weapons had to be reduced. By various artfully arranged mechanical contrivances, the lens could be made to present and escape from the eye above the cornea when a certain spot on the sclerotic was touched, and the cornea then roll back into position. Ingenious as

PLATE XXIII.

A. QUARRY SILCOCK.

[To face p. 167

all these contrivances were, the effect of the model when exhibited was to excite mirth more than anything else. It passed into the possession of the Hospital after Streatfield's death, but no further use was made of it.

A. Quarry Silcock was elected to succeed Streatfield; besides being an ophthalmic surgeon he was a general surgeon attached to St. Mary's Hospital. At one time, as has been shown, all members of the surgical staff of the Hospital had to be either a general surgeon or a demonstrator of anatomy connected with a general hospital. This rule had, however, been altered, it being thought only necessary to insist on candidates possessing the diploma of Fellowship of the College of Surgeons of England, as a guarantee that they had attained a high standard of general surgical efficiency. Silcock was the last member of the staff appointed who combined the practice of ophthalmology with that of general surgery; all those since appointed, though Fellows of the College of Surgeons, have restricted their practice to ophthalmology. With the growth of knowledge the speciality of ophthalmology had come to consist of much besides mere dexterity in the performance of certain surgical operations. Here may be aptly quoted what the late Dr. James Anderson wrote with reference to it in 1889:

" It seems to me the best and most hopeful feature of ophthalmology that it has relations, closer or more remote, with every branch of medicine and surgery—indeed, with almost every branch of science."

CHAPTER XI

THE SELECTION OF A NEW SITE, AND THE ERECTION OF THE NEW HOSPITAL

The condition of the Moorfields Hospital in 1884 may be compared to that of a man wearing a suit of clothes fitted to him in his youth, which had since been added to, patched, and darned, to cover his nakedness. The result was that he not only presented an incongruous appearance, but lived in constant fear of fresh dilapidations.

To carry the analogy still further, those who would be called upon to find funds for a fresh suit, and who had taken pains to make the patches, desired to leave matters as they were. Whilst the man himself, who had to wear and work in his old-fashioned clothes, was all agog for a new rig-out.

The Hospital erected in 1821 was in keeping with the conceptions of the time and adapted for the accommodation then required. With the new ideas which arose out of Florence Nightingale's teaching, and later as the outcome of bacteriological investigations, the general principles for hospital construction became completely changed. Though the original Moorfields Hospital was added to and altered to meet new requirements, it became obvious to the rising generation of medical men working there that it could never be converted into an up-to-date institution. It took time, however, before the Committee of Management as a body could be induced to look at the matter in the same light, especially its older members who had taken part in raising funds and arranging for the additions.

In 1884 a piece of building land in Eldon Street to the west of the Hospital became vacant, and the Controller of the City of London offered to lay any proposal the Committee of Management might feel inclined to make concerning it before the Bridge House Estates Committee. Though urged by the Medical Council to acquire it, the Committee of Management replied that it did not feel able to tender.

During the next three years circumstances arose which gradually convinced the Committee that there were irremediable defects in the Hospital as regards accommodation, ventilation and sanitation. The beds were always full, and the waiting-list of patients requiring in-patient treatment grew in dimensions. The cubic space per patient in the wards was very deficient, and no cross-ventilation of them was possible. There were no day rooms in which patients not confined to bed could take their meals. There was no passenger lift to convey patients who had been operated on to the upper floors, so that they had to walk up a narrow staircase. There were no bath rooms, and very inefficient accommodation, for the resident staff. The drainage, laid down without any general plan, and in piecemeal fashion, was constantly being attended to and tinkered with.

In 1887 the Medical Council complained of the defective sanitation of the Hospital, and requested that a sanitary expert might be asked to examine the drainage and advise in the matter. At the same time it submitted to the Committee a report entitled, *Some Defects in the Royal London Ophthalmic Hospital,* in which the above mentioned deficiencies and others were set out in detail. From the consideration of this report, and that received from the sanitary expert, it became obvious that nothing but a new building would meet all the requirements.

The building land in the rear of the Hospital facing Eldon Street still remained temptingly vacant, and, in 1887, a suggestion was received, emanating from the City architect, that an exchange might possibly be effected—*i.e.,* the taking of the existing site of the Hospital for the vacant site in Eldon Street together with a sum of £15,000.

Though this suggestion did not come to anything, it served to awaken the Committee of Management to the valuable assets the Hospital possessed in the greatly enhanced value of its freehold and leasehold properties, due to the changes which had taken place in its environment since it was first built—unearned increment, which was eventually put to the best possible use by an extension of the means for the relief of suffering in the community.

Mr. Lander, the Hospital's surveyor, was then requested to obtain valuations of the Hospital's site and of that of the vacant land adjoining it. No very precise figures were obtained, the site of the Hospital being valued at anything between £50,000 and £100,000. The Committee still, however, hesitated to make any tender for the vacant land.

In July, 1888, after a consultation of representatives of the Medical Council with Sir John Lubbock, the President of the Hospital, he agreed to introduce a deputation to the Lord Mayor to request him to use his influence in obtaining for the Hospital a gift of the vacant land adjoining it from the Corporation. The Lord Mayor pointed out that it was trust property held by the Bridge House Estates, which had no power to comply with the appeal of the deputation " so earnestly and reasonably made." The deputation next waited on the Bridge House Estates Committee, who replied that it was unable to pledge itself not to accept any tender, but the matter would receive its most favourable consideration.

Matters were still further advanced in that year: firstly, by the receipt of an unsolicited donation of fifty guineas from the trustees of St. Stephen's, Coleman Street, towards a Building Fund, which led to the opening of such a fund for subscriptions, to which the surgeons of the Hospital in the following year promised a gift of £1,000; secondly, by the desire of the City to effect a street improvement, so as to widen the junction of Blomfield Street and Eldon Street, which would necessitate a surrender of a slice of the Hospital's ground.

A complication arose, due to the Hospital's land not directly adjoining that vacant in Eldon Street—a Welsh chapel, with a lease of four years yet to run, intervening between them.

Ultimately, the Bridge House Estates Committee offered the Hospital the vacant area, including that of the Welsh chapel, comprising in all 7,180 feet, on lease for ninety-nine years at a peppercorn rent of £311 per annum until the chapel's lease expired, and then at £388 per annum, with, however, the provision that the Committee of the Hospital or its trustees were made personally responsible for the payment of the rent and the observance of the conditions of the lease. This provision neither the members of the Committee nor the trustees of the Hospital were prepared to accept, and the whole of the year 1889 was spent in endeavouring to come to terms with the Law Guarantee and Trust Society to take on these responsibilities. These negotiations not proving satisfactory, it was decided, in 1890, that application should be made to the Privy Council for a Charter of Incorporation. A Petition for Incorporating the Hospital by Royal Charter was prepared and presented to Her Majesty the Queen in Council, together with a draft form of the Charter which would empower the Hospital to hold land in mortmain, and thereby enable it to proceed with negotiations for the lease. The Charter of Incorporation under the Great Seal was passed in December, 1890, to which a common seal, that had been designed for the Hospital, was appended.

In the lease obtained for the ground in Eldon Street it was laid down that building was to commence before January, 1893, and it became necessary at once to appoint a suitable architect to draw up plans. Messrs. Lander

and Bedell were at that time acting as surveyors to the
Hospital, but hospital construction had developed into a
very specialised branch of architecture, and it was thought
desirable to employ for the new building one who had a
large experience of that kind of work. In August, 1891,
Mr. Keith Young, who had already designed several hospitals, was appointed, to be assisted by Mr. Lander, and
after his death in 1892 by Mr. Bedell.

After due and deliberate consideration, the architects
arrived at the opinion that the site, even including that of
the Welsh chapel, would not allow of sufficient space to
meet all the requirements of the new Hospital. They
suggested that a larger one might be acquired in a less
valuable locality. Investigations were made, and a site
which seemed to offer many advantages was discovered in
the City Road. Many of those associated with the Hospital
felt very loath to move the Institution from the neighbourhood of Moorfields, with which it had become so intimately
associated. The matter was discussed at length at a joint
meeting of the Committee of Management and the medical
staff, and in July, 1892, the latter passed the following
resolution:

" That considering the alleged great value of the present
site and the difficulty of constructing a suitable building
upon it, the Medical Council is of opinion that the present
site should be sold and that, so far as the information at
present at its disposal goes, the City Road site is best
adapted for a new Hospital provided that the whole of that
site can be acquired."

With the sanction of the Bridge House Estates Committee, the lease of the Eldon Street site with all its obligation was transferred to a substantial tenant, who was willing
to pay the Hospital a premium of £1,000.

The lease was then obtained for 999 years from March,
1894, of what was termed the City Road and Peerless Street
site of some 35,000 feet, in the parish of St. Luke's, Old

Street, in the county of Middlesex, at a rent of £1,210 per annum; from the Ecclesiastical Commissioners.

It is rather a remarkable coincidence that another hospital, which was originally situated at Moorfields, should have previously removed to the neighbourhood of the City Road, and not very far from the Peerless Street site. St. Luke's Hospital, which, though independent of Bethlehem Hospital, dealt with the same class of ailments, was originally established in 1750 on the north side of Moorfields. In 1782 a new building was erected near the junction of Old Street and the City Road, it being recorded that at that time green fields could be seen in every direction. The building continued as a hospital for the mentally defective until the time of the Great War, when it was taken over by the Bank of England, of which it continues to be a branch.

Peerless Street runs between the City Road and Bath Street. It is lined by a row of small, mean houses, which, but for the Rent Restriction Act, would have been swept away ere this by the ground landlord, St. Bartholomew's Hospital. Anyone unacquainted with the history of the neighbourhood may well wonder how such a poverty-stricken street could have acquired such a high-sounding name. It is the last remaining sign of the delectable attractions which formerly existed in its neighbourhood.

In ancient times some springs overflowed and formed a pond between what is now Peerless Street and St. Luke's Hospital; from it water was conducted through pipes to Lothbury for the benefit of the inhabitants of that district. Stowe describes it in 1603 as " cleare water called the Perilous Pond because divers youths by swimming therein have been drowned." In consequence of such accidents (the inhabitants of Lothbury having obtained water from elsewhere), the Perilous Pond was entirely filled in. In 1743 Mr. William Kemp, an eminent jeweller and citizen of London, having derived relief from violent pains in the head from which he had suffered for several years by bathing in the water from the spring, converted it into what William Maitland, in his *History of London*, 1775, describes as " the completest swimming bath in the whole world." " He spared," Maitland says, " no expense nor contrivances to render it quite private and retired from public inspection, decent in its regulations and as genteel in its furniture as such a place could be made." At the same time he changed its name from the disagreeable one of the " Perilous Pond," which it no longer was, to the pleasing one of the " Peerless Pool," which, owing to its size and surroundings, it had undoubtedly become. The swimming bath measured 170 feet in length and 100 feet in width, and varied from 5 to 3 feet in depth. The entrance to it was through a marble pavilion 30 feet in length and across a bowling green; it was surrounded by dressing compartments, outside which were lofty banks covered with shrubs and a terraced walk planted with lime trees. Four pairs of marble steps descended to the bath, which had a fine gravel bottom. Besides this open swimming bath, there was a covered cold bath, supplied with water from a specially cold spring, faced with marble and paved with stone. The most remarkable feature, however, of the Peerless Pool was " a noble fish pond constructed by Kemp due east and west. It was 320 feet long, 93 feet broad, and 11 feet deep, stocked with carp, tench, and a great variety of the finney tribe, wherein subscribers and frequenters of either the pleasure or the cold bath were privileged to angle." William Hone, in his *Every-day Book*, published in 1831, gives engravings of the fish pond (showing the lime walk and Kemp's house in the distance) and of the swimming bath, made by Mr. John Cleghorn, an architectural draftsman and engraver, who for many years resided near the Pool.

In the *Daily Advertiser* of August, 1748, are some doggerel verses extolling the attractions of the Peerless Pool, and also a statement that—

PLATE XXIV.

THE PLEASURE BATH,
PEERLESS POOL, CITY ROAD.

TERMS OF	SUBSCRIPTION.
PLEASURE BATH	COLD BATH

PLEASURE BATH

	£. s d
Month	0 9 0
Two Months	0 10 0
Year	1 1 0
Single Baths with Towels and Box .. }	0 1 0
Ditto without	0 0 6

COLD BATH

	£ s d
Month.....	0 10 0
Two Months	0 17 0
Year	1 10 0
Single Baths	0 1 0

1 Bath Buildings Entrance—2, Baldwyn Street Entrance—3, Cold Bath—4, Pleasure Bath—5, Dressing Boxes—6, Shrubberies.

THE PLEASURE BATH
OF PEERLESS POOL,

THE largest in England, is situated in the immediate neighbourhood of the heart of the City, within Ten minutes' direct walk of the Bank and Exchange. (vide plan.) Surrounded by trees and shrubberies, open to the air, although entirely screened from observation, and most ample in its dimensions—**170** FEET in length, by **108** in breadth—it offers to the Bather the very advantages he would least expect to find at so short a distance from the centre of the metropolis. Its depth, which increases gradually from 3 feet 6 inches to 4 feet 8 inches, is such as to afford free scope to the Swimmer, while it precludes all fear of accident to any and the temperature of the water rises to a height sufficient to ensure all the comfort and luxury of Bathing, without the risk of injury to health, from a too violent contrast with the external air.

THE COLD BATH,

THIRTY-SIX feet by EIGHTEEN, is the largest of its kind in London, and both Baths are entirely supplied by Springs, which are constantly overflowing.

The City Road is the line from all parts of the WEST END to the City. Omnibuses pass both ways nearly every minute throughout the day

BILL OF PEERLESS POOL. *Cir.* 1846.

[To face p. 175

" any gentleman, who subscribes only one guinea per annum, is entitled to the pleasure and cold bath, and to the diversion of angling and skating at proper seasons; and that if any occasional visitor, who must pay 2s. each time he bathes, thinks proper to become a subscriber in the fourteen days from his first visit, he shall be allowed that he has paid it as part of his subscription."

After Kemp's death the Pool seems to have changed hands several times. On the expiration of the lease in 1805, a new one was obtained from St. Bartholomew's Hospital by Mr. Joseph Watt, at an annual rental of £600. To remunerate himself Mr. Watt drained the fish pond, felled the trees around it, and built Baldwin Street, which lies just south of Peerless Street, on its former site. He also erected Bath Buildings on the ground occupied by Kemp's orchard, but left the pleasure bath intact. In 1831 William Hone wrote:

" The pleasure bath is still a pleasant spot, and both that and the cold bath retain their ancient capabilities. Indeed, the attractions of the pleasure bath are undiminished. Its size is the same as in Kemp's time, and trees enough remain to shade the visitor from the heat of the sun while on the brink, irresolute whether to plunge gloriously in, or ignobly walk down the steps. . . . Every fine Thursday and Saturday afternoon in the summer, columns of blue-coat boys, more than three score in each, headed by their respective beadles, arrive, and some half strip themselves ere they reach their destination; the rapid plunge they make into the pool, and their hilarity in the bath, testify their enjoyment of the tepid fluid."

The Peerless Pool continued in existence as a public bath until 1850, the site occupied by it being built over between that date and 1860.

Out of the City Road, on the opposite side to Peerless Street, leads Shepherdess Walk, which marks the site of the Shepherd and Shepherdess ale-house and tea-garden, built some time before 1745. The gardens were frequented by visitors who regaled themselves with cream, cakes and

fromity.   Invalids sometimes stayed at the inn to benefit
by the pure air of the neighbourhood.

> " To the Shepherd and Shepherdess then they go
>   To tea with their wives, for a constant rule;
>   And next cross the road to the Fountain also,
>   And there they all sit, so pleasant and cool,
>   And see, in and out,
>   The folk walk about,
>   And the gentlemen angling in Peerless Pool."

In Baldwin Street there is still a public-house called " The
Fountain," which is probably the survival of the one referred
to in this old rhyme, and of one which Franklin wrote of, " a
very genteel public house at the east end of Kemp's garden."

The City Road, which was opened in 1761, cut through
the meadow grounds which surrounded the Shepherd and
Shepherdess, so that the place lost its rural isolation.   The
inn was pulled down in 1825, and the Eagle Tavern, which
formed the nucleus of the famous Eagle establishment,
with its Grecian saloon and theatre, and its garden and
dancing pavilion, was erected near its site.   It was this
establishment which was celebrated in the refrain of the
popular song:

> " Up and down the City Road,
>   In and out the Eagle,
>   That's the way the money goes,
>   Pop goes the weasel."

It has been suggested that this refrain might be para-
phrased by those employed at the Moorfields Hospital as
follows:

> " Up and down the City Road,
>   In and out Moorfields,
>   That's the way we spend our lives,
>   Oh ! the joy it yields."

Whilst the above discussions and negotiations with regard
to the erection of a new Hospital were in progress several
changes took place in the personnel of the staff.

In 1890 John Whitaker Hulke, having reached the age of sixty, retired. He died five years later whilst holding the highest position in his profession, that of President of the Royal College of Surgeons in England. John Browning Lawford, who had already held the posts of house surgeon and of curator of the Museum, was elected in his place.

In 1891 George Lawson also had to retire under the age limit rule. In 1869 he had published a *Manual on Diseases and Injuries of the Eye*, which, owing to its practical character, became exceedingly popular amongst medical students, and rapidly ran through five editions. Lawson endeared himself to his patients by the personal interest he manifested in their welfare. His treatment went far beyond the mere prescription of drugs or the performance of operations. He would instruct a mother how to feed, clothe, and train her child. He would tell a patient, for whom nothing could be done to restore the lost sight, what his future might be and how to get to work to earn a livelihood. Many of those engaged in seeing out-patients often wish they could prescribe food for them instead of medicine. Lawson actually did this, having an arrangement with a neighbouring butcher by which he could at his own expense order patients so many pounds of meat. Nor did his generosity to Hospital patients end with supplying sound advice and meat; many to whom some unusually disastrous circumstance had occurred would be led quietly aside and return with a smiling face and a closed palm.

In 1886 Lawson was appointed surgeon oculist to Her Majesty Queen Victoria, which appointment he held until her death. He himself died in 1903 at the age of seventy-two, having had the satisfaction of seeing his son Arnold (now Sir Arnold Lawson) appointed on the staff at Moorfields, where he himself had worked for so long.

The vacancy caused by Lawson's retirement was filled by the election of A. Stanford Morton, who was educated at Edinburgh University. He had served the Hospital first as house surgeon and later as clinical assistant for a period of sixteen years. He did not take the necessary qualification of the Fellowship of the Royal College of Surgeons of England, which would qualify him as a candidate for the staff, until 1888, and was forty-eight years of age at the time of his election. His name has become widely known throughout the ophthalmic world in connection with the very serviceable and popular pattern of ophthalmoscope which he had constructed for him by Messrs. Curry and Paxton. It happily combined all the best features and adaptations which had previously been suggested.

For dexterity and neatness as an operator on the eye Morton was unsurpassed in his time. He enthusiastically instructed others in the art, holding classes of operative ophthalmic surgery in which he employed pigs' eyes fixed in a frame to enable students to obtain the necessary manipulative dexterity. Whilst he was working as a clinical assistant, the practice of retinoscopy for the correction of errors of refraction came into use, and he wrote a small book on *Refraction of the Eye*, describing it in such an easily assimilated manner that the book had a large sale, several editions being called for.

Being a good draftsman, and having an excellent eye for colour, Morton made many beautiful coloured drawings of ophthalmoscopic changes, the originals of which he presented to the Hospital on his retirement. The extreme care which he took in their production often necessitated several sittings on the part of the patient. In one interesting and complicated case, the drawing of which took a very long time, Morton found it necessary to remunerate the patient liberally after each sitting to ensure his subsequent attendance. When the drawing was finished the man found that Morton's interest in his case had evaporated, and, being hard up, appeared at the Hospital one morning offering to sell him one of his eyes if he would like to take it out—an offer which it is perhaps needless to say was not accepted.

The man afterwards went about to various ophthalmic clinics calling himself the celebrated Moorfields case, and he informed those who examined him " that gentlemen generally gave him something after looking at the backs of his eyes."

Though it had been the custom for a long time to print on the letters given to patients, and to have posted up in the out-patient department, a notice to the effect that the Hospital was only open for the reception of really indigent patients, it was a rule which the medical staff found very difficult to enforce, and which was obviously very frequently infringed. In 1893, on the advice of the Medical Council, the Committee of Management adopted the plan in use at several of the other London hospitals of appointing an " inquiry officer " to attend daily and make necessary inquiries, so that " no person should be admitted in the first instance to Hospital relief who can afford to pay a fee of one guinea for a consultation (except in cases of accident)." The officer appointed for this purpose was one selected by the Charity Organisation Society, who had been trained under its superintendance. As the result of his investigations, from about 500 applicants were refused yearly, it being found that they were able to pay a surgeon's fee, many of them stating that they were unaware that the Hospital was open for the poor only.

John Couper's time for retirement from the staff came in 1895. He continued in active practice for several years afterwards, and died in 1918, in his eighty-third year. He had always been a firm supporter of the movement for the admission of women to the medical profession, and welcomed Miss Elizabeth Garrett (afterwards Mrs. Garrett Anderson) as an onlooker at his clinic at Moorfields. It was not, however, until after he had left the staff, in 1898, that the eligibility of women to become pupils and clinical assistants at the Hospital became officially recognised.

E. Treacher Collins, who, like Lawford, had been both

house surgeon and curator of the Museum at the Hospital, was appointed as Couper's successor.

The premature and unexpected resignation from the staff of Edward Nettleship took place in 1898; his keen interest in the scientific side of ophthalmology, however, did not slacken. He gave the Hospital a donation of £250, to be expended on scientific apparatus and appliances for the laboratory in the new building. With more time at his disposal for research work, his valuable scientific contributions increased in number. With indefatigable ardour and strenuous accuracy he worked out pedigrees of hereditary diseases, the value of which work was recognised in 1912 by his election as a Fellow of the Royal Society. On his retirement from practice in 1901, his friends and pupils inaugurated a fund to found the " Edward Nettleship Prize " for the encouragement of scientific ophthalmic work. It took the form of a Gold Medal to be awarded at intervals, at the discretion of the Council of the Ophthalmological Society, British subjects alone being eligible. He died in October, 1913, being actively employed up to the time of his death, in conjunction with Karl Pearson and C. H. Usher, on a large monograph upon " Albinism in Man."

To fill the surprise vacancy caused by Nettleship's retirement, W. T. Holmes Spicer was appointed.

Three matrons at the Hospital resigned from ill-health in the course of a few years, and, in 1895, Miss Ada Robertson, a former sister at the London Hospital, was appointed to the post. She not only carried through the difficult task of transferring the work of the Hospital from the old to the new building, but also, with skill and tact, raised the nursing to a higher standard of efficiency than it had reached before.

In 1897 Mr. Charles Gordon, who had acted as Chairman of the Committee of Management for eighteen years, and who had taken an active part in all the negotiations for the removal of the Hospital to a new site, on the eve of the laying of the foundation stone, found it incumbent upon him to resign owing to his advanced years; he died two years later. Thus, like Moses, having led his colleagues to within sight of the promised land, he left it for them to enter into its occupation.

Mr. H. P. Sturgis, a director of the London and Westminster Bank, was elected Chairman in his place.

About the same time, Mr. Robert J. Newstead, after twenty-five years' service as secretary, had to resign from ill-health, and died at the end of the year. Mr. Robert J. Bland was appointed as his successor.

On the 28th of May, 1897, the work of clearing and preparing the foundations being sufficiently advanced, His Royal Highness the Prince of Wales (afterwards King Edward VII.), on behalf of Her Majesty Queen Victoria, laid the foundation stone of the new Hospital. His Royal Highness was accompanied by their Royal Highnesses the Princess of Wales (afterwards Queen Alexandra) and Princess Victoria, the former graciously consenting to receive purses containing donations in aid of the Hospital. The silver trowel used on the occasion, which was provided by Mr. E. Hogg, one of the members of the Committee of Management, was presented to His Royal Highness, who stated " it is Her Majesty's great and earnest wish that this Hospital may be prosperous and successful in every way." Her Majesty further manifested her continual interest in the Charity by giving a donation of £100 to the Building Fund. The Prince of Wales on his departure signified his intention to become a Patron of the Hospital.

In the removal of the Hospital from a prominent situation which had developed into a great business centre to a less known district easily accessible to those to whose needs it ministered, the Committee of Management hoped to defray the cost of the building by the proceeds of the sale of the old site, and in doing so it was not far out in its reckoning. The old Hospital was sold for £78,500, and the new Hospital cost about £80,000. To provide the funds for the new building, whilst the work was being carried on in the old one, large loans had to be negotiated on the security of its freehold and leasehold property. In addition to the cost of the building the Committee had to provide funds for furnishing the new building, and equipping it with appliances and apparatus in keeping with its position as the leading ophthalmic institution in the British Empire. For this purpose it made a special appeal which was liberally responded to by the Corporation of the City of London and the following City Companies: The Worshipful Company of Carpenters, of Clothworkers, of Drapers, of Dyers, of Fishmongers, of Goldsmiths, of Grocers, of Leather Sellers, of Mercers, of Merchant Taylors, of Sadlers, of Salters, and of Skinners.

The fund was further augmented by a festival dinner held at the Grand Hotel, Charing Cross, on the 6th of May, 1898, over which His Royal Highness the Duke of Cambridge graciously presided, he himself making a liberal contribution to the cause for which he pleaded. In the following year a large and influential number of ladies promoted a ball in the Empress Rooms at the Royal Palace Hotel, Kensington, on the Hospital's behalf, and Sir Squire Bancroft generously gave to it the proceeds of one of his inimitable readings.

When the clearance of the site for the new Hospital in the City Road was commenced, a Building Committee was appointed, consisting of certain members of the Committee of Management, with Mr. H. Davidson as chairman, and three representatives of the Medical Council, Tweedy, Gunn, and its honorary secretary, at first Morton, and later Treacher Collins.

One of the first questions this Committee had to consider was the dual one of the ventilation and warming of the new building. Was the system of ventilation to be " natural " or " artificial " ? If artificial, was it to take the form of propulsion or extraction, or a combination of both ? It has been well said " that theories in ventilation and warming are as numerous as trees in a forest," and so the Building Committee discovered when they commenced to consider the problem. Several hospitals in which artificial ventilation was in use were inspected; ultimately it was decided that artificial ventilation on the planum system should be adopted for the out-patient department, and that natural ventilation should be relied upon for the wards.

The air forced into the out-patient department is first filtered, and then warmed or cooled as required. A shaft is provided which allows the foul air to escape. The force employed is a large rotating fan-wheel which propels the air along underground passages, and through gratings which open into the various compartments. It is filtered by passing through a coke-screen, which is cleaned with a stream of water flowing over it automatically at periodic intervals. It is warmed by passing over hot-water radiators situated close to the gratings opening into the compartments. It can be cooled by substituting blocks of ice placed on the radiators for the hot water contained in them.

In the wards the position of the windows is arranged to allow of cross ventilation, and the main sources of heat are open fires. Additional sources for warmth and ventilation are provided by hot water radiators, past which fresh air is allowed to enter through gratings near the floor. A separate sanitary block running through the centre of the building is cut off from it by cross-ventilation lobbies.

Only those who worked in the old Hospital in Blomfield Street can fully appreciate the amenities afforded by the new one in the City Road. Daily at noon the whole in-patient department in the old building became permeated with the odour of cooked meat. In the new Hospital all such disagreeable smells have been avoided by having the kitchen placed on the top floor. Most of the cooking is carried on by steam, supplied from boilers in the basement.

A special service lift conveys goods to the kitchen, and also permits of the distribution of food and fuel to various parts of the building. Both this lift and the passenger lift are worked by hydraulic power; the latter allows of the conveyance of a patient on a wheeled trolley, in the recumbent position, to his bed from the operating table.

The lighting arrangements in the out-patient department, for the examination of the patients and the testing of their eyesight, and in the operating theatre to meet its varied requirements, engaged the architect's and the Committee's prolonged consideration. For the examination of patients in the first instance, and for many operations, uninterrupted direct skylight from a northern aspect was regarded as essential, and the new building was so planned as to allow of this in the large consulting room and in the operating theatre. As the work of the Hospital has to be carried out on dark days as well as bright ones, adequate means for the examination of patients by artificial light, in the absence of daylight, had to be provided. In the old Hospital, where gas was the main source of artificial illumination, there were various contrivances rendering it more or less efficient by the use of reflectors. In the operating theatre, a device used by the Nottingham lace workers had been employed. It consisted of a large hollow glass globe filled with water and suspended from the ceiling, which concentrated light from a lamp placed behind it on to the face of a patient lying on the operating table. The introduction of electricity for illuminating purposes throughout the new building simplified matters considerably. In the consulting room, movable flexes and adjustments permit light being easily brought into the most suitable position in which to conduct an examination. The employment of electric light globes for ophthalmoscopic examinations in the dark room, in place of argand gas burners, renders the atmosphere in it far more healthy and pleasant to work in, but it is doubtful if any form of electric bulb supplies quite such a uniform and satisfactory area of illumination for these examinations as the old argand gas burner.

The electric current supplied to the Hospital for lighting purposes is an alternating one; fortunately a constant current was also available in the district, being used in neighbouring factories. One of the chief purposes for which it is required is for working electro-magnets for the extraction of chips of iron or steel implanted in the interior of the eyeball.

It has been already mentioned how in 1858 Dixon tried unsuccessfully to remove a chip off the edge of a chisel, seen floating in the vitreous chamber, by a permanent magnet. In a similar case, McKeown of Belfast, in 1874, succeeded in the removal of the foreign body by the introduction of the tip of a permanent magnet into the interior of the eye.

In 1878 Malcolm McHardy, who was later ophthalmic surgeon to King's College Hospital, employed for the first time an electro-magnet, and with it successfully removed a chip of steel which had become embedded in the crystalline lens. A few years later, Snell of Sheffield, Hirschberg of Berlin, and Bradford of Boston, U.S.A., had constructed electro-magnets which could be held in the hand, and have suitable terminals attached to them for introduction into the interior of the eye. Considerable success attended the use of such instruments when fragments of iron were situated in the front parts of the eye, but only on rare occasions when they had become deeply placed in the vitreous humour. In these latter cases, the foreign body was often hid from view, due to opacity of the lens caused by the injury, so that its exact position was unknown, and there was some doubt as to whether it had lodged in the eyeball or not. It was only when the nozzle of the hand magnet came close to the foreign body that it possessed sufficient traction power to draw it out, and in searching for it much damage was liable to be inflicted on the structures in the interior of the eyeball.

On the discovery of the X-rays by Professor Röntgen in
1895 it occurred to many ophthalmic surgeons that they
might be utilised for the detection of foreign bodies in the
eye. Two practical difficulties at first presented themselves, both of which were ultimately overcome. One was
the density of the bony structures around the eyeball, and
the other that of locating accurately the position of a foreign
body when detected. It was found that excellent skiagrams,
showing exceedingly minute pieces of metallic substances
in the orbit, could be obtained if the sensitive plate was
placed against the temple on the side of the injured eye, and
the Crookes tube 10 to 15 mm. distant from the opposite
temple. The most accurate localisation of foreign bodies
implanted in the body was effected by an ingenious device
of Mackenzie Davidson's in which, after superimposing
two skiagrams taken at slightly different positions, he followed the tract taken by the rays from the Crookes tube
to the foreign body by means of threads, noting where they
crossed in relation to the position of other known points.

Mackenzie Davidson (afterwards Sir James Mackenzie
Davidson) worked at Moorfields as clinical assistant, and
subsequently practised as an ophthalmic surgeon in Aber-
deen. Soon after the discovery of X-rays, he removed
to London and devoted himself specially to their application to surgery and medicine. His combined interest in
ophthalmology and X-rays made him desirous of testing
his method of localising foreign bodies in connection with
eye injuries. Several members of the staff at Moorfields
sent cases to him to report on, and such accurate and helpful
information did he supply, not only as to the presence or
absence of a foreign body in the eye, but also as to the
exact position in which, when present, it could be found,
that a desire arose to establish a special X-ray department
and to secure his services in connection therewith. On the
recommendation of the Medical Council, this was agreed to
by the Committee of Management in November, 1898, £80

being voted for the cost of apparatus and an annual expenditure of £20 for the working expenses of the department. Mackenzie Davidson consented to accept the appointment of honorary medical officer in charge of the X-ray department, and a special room was fitted up in the new Hospital with the necessary conveniences for carrying on the work.

The introduction of the constant electric current into the operating theatre allowed of the employment of f r more powerful magnets for the extraction of fragments of iron from the eyeball than had previously been used in this country. These powerful magnets have appropriately been described as " giant magnets ": they were originally introduced into ophthalmic practice by Professor Haab of Zurich. Their traction force is so great that a chip of iron hidden in the back part of the eyeball can be drawn forward into view in the front part.

In the *Hospital Reports*, H. V. McKenzie, the house surgeon in 1895, collected notes of all the cases in which a foreign body had been removed from the eye by the small hand magnet—*i.e.*, prior to the introduction of X-ray localisation, and found that in 26 per cent. of those in which it was lodged in the vitreous the eye was saved. In 1902 the house surgeon, A. F. MacCallan, tabulated the results obtained by the use of Haab's Giant Magnet, and found that in a similar class of cases by its use 58 per cent. of the eyes were saved, and that in half of these good vision was obtained. If accurate localisation of the foreign body by X-rays was carried out previous to the use of the magnet, a still larger percentage of success resulted.

The operating theatre in the new Hospital has been designed to make possible the practice of aseptic surgery. Antiseptic surgery, as first introduced, relied on the destruction of micro-organisms by chemical agents, and it was thought essential, whilst an operation was in progress, to have a spray of carbolic acid playing to prevent aerial infection of the wound. Later, as the result of experience gained in bacteriological laboratories, it became realised that such a precaution was unnecessary; micro-organisms being like dust particles subject to the law of gravitation, all that was required was to prevent any accumulation of dust and to avoid currents of air.

To avoid any accumulation of dust in the new operating theatre, its walls, ceilings, and floor are so constructed that at any time they can be washed over with a hose.   The wall and ceiling are lined with glass tiles, technically known as "opalite," the floor is paved with terazzo, and all the corners are rounded.   All the pipes are of copper, and the radiators of the same metal.   The latter are constructed so that they can be swung out on a pivot, and no dirt be allowed to accumulate behind them; they are in three divisions, which allow of variations in the amount of warmth given out as may be required.

To permit as many onlookers as possible being able to watch the operator's procedures, without inconveniencing him or his assistants, fixed stands are erected on each side of the operating table, each stand being composed of three tiers, and each tier accommodating four persons.

The colour of the tiles on the walls and ceiling is a creamy-white with a dado of pale green.   As some operations have to be conducted in a darkened room by artificial light concentrated on the eye, a dark blind is provided which can be drawn up from below, being enclosed when not in use in a brass box.

The case in which the instruments are stored is constructed entirely of brass and glass, and apparatus is provided to allow of the instruments being sterilised by boiling them before use.   A special steriliser for dressings is also provided, with an outer jacket for steam, which permits of them being delivered dry when required for use.

In the wards, passages, and other parts of the building, all possible precautions are taken to avoid any lodgments for the accumulation of dust, the floors of all the wards being constructed of polished teak, and wherever possible the corners are rounded. All cupboards have sloping tops, and are fixed to the walls at such a height that the highest part of them is easily within reach. Arrangements are made for the storage of the patients' clothes, when in bed, in special cupboards outside the wards, and the small marble-topped lockers placed beside their beds were specially designed just to contain a few of their possessions.

A special eye hospital differs from a general hospital in the large proportion of its patients who are able to be up out of bed during the daytime. It is, therefore, desirable to have special day rooms in which they can congregate away from the wards, and have their meals. In the new Hospital, on each floor, such day room accommodation is provided.

Notwithstanding the enormous amount of work involved in the removal to the new building, it was effected with scarcely any interruption in the routine work of the Institution. The new building was opened for the reception of patients on September 4th, 1899, the work in the old Hospital being carried on for in-patients up to August 19th, and for out-patients up to August 26th.

CHAPTER XII

THE HOSPITAL IN THE CITY ROAD

On June 28th, 1899, the now dreary neighbourhood of the former " Peerless Pool " once again awoke to life and notoriety with a visit from their present Majesties King George V. and Queen Mary, then the Duke and Duchess of York, to open the new " Peerless " Eye Hospital. A lengthy description of the ceremony appeared in *The Times* on the following day.

The Duke and Duchess of York, attended by Sir Charles Cust and Lady Katherine Coke, arrived at the Hospital shortly after half-past 3 o'clock, and were received by Sir John Lubbock, the President, Mr. H. P. Sturgis, Chairman of the Committee of Management, and the architects, Messrs. Keith Young and H. Hall. The Duke, who received a gold key from the architects, unlocked the door of the main entrance hall, where the surgeons of the Hospital, the matron, Miss Robinson, and the secretary, Mr. R. J. Bland, were presented to their Royal Highnesses. The Royal party were then conducted over the building, and after completing their inspection they entered the out-patients' hall, which had been prettily decorated for the opening ceremony, and where a large company had assembled. Among the visitors, in addition to those already named, were the Lord Mayor and Lady Mayoress, Mr. Alderman and Sheriff Alliston, Lieutenant-Colonel and Sheriff Probyn and Mrs. Probyn, the Bishop of Islington and Mrs. Turner, the Rev. Prebendary Whittington (chaplain), Sir J. Whittaker Ellis and Lady Ellis, Lady Faudel-Phillips, Sir Squire and Lady Bancroft, Mr. J. Lea Smith (trustee), Mrs. Sturgis, Sir T. Lipton, and the Rev. Dr. Hermann Adler and Mrs.

PLATE XXV.

THE ROYAL LONDON OPHTHALMIC HOSPITAL IN THE CITY ROAD, OPENED IN 1899.

[To face p. 190

Adler, Mr. H. Davison (chairman of the Building Committee) and Mrs. Davison, Mr. A. G. Pollock (chairman
of the Special Appeal Committee) and Mrs. Pollock.   The
little daughter of Mr. John Tweedy, the senior surgeon,
presented a handsome bouquet of pink roses to the Duchess,
who was dressed in pale green eau de Nil silk with a toque
of pink roses.   Prayers having been said by the Bishop of
Islington, Sir John Lubbock called upon Mr. Sturgis to
make a statement.

Mr. Sturgis said that they valued extremely the presence
of the Duke and Duchess of York, inasmuch as their Royal
Highnesses represented the fourth generation of the Royal
Family who had shown interest in the Hospital.   He related
the circumstances which had necessitated its removal from
its old site at Moorfields and the erection of the present
building, which the Committee had endeavoured to make as
perfect as possible, and which they would come into free
from debt.   This, however, he went on to say, was only
the beginning of their task.   They had to consider the
maintenance of the establishment.   The cost of maintenance
at the old building was about £8,000 a year, and their regular
income, including grants from the Hospital funds, did not
reach the sum of £3,000 a year, so that they had to make
up the difference in other ways.   But the cost of maintenance in the new building would be as much as £11,000
a year.   He hoped their income would increase to a corresponding extent.   What they wanted more than anything
else was an increase in annual subscriptions, and they
wished to raise a fund of £50,000 which would be a guarantee
for the large ground rent which they now had to pay.

Sir John Lubbock, after expressing indebtedness to all
those concerned in the work of the Institution, asked the
Duke of York to declare the building open.

The Duke of York said:

" Sir John Lubbock, Mr. Sturgis, Ladies and Gentlemen,
I am grateful to Sir John Lubbock for the kind words he

has used with regard to our coming here to-day, and I have been very much interested in all I have heard from Mr. Sturgis, the Chairman of the Committee. I thank you all in the Duchess' name as well as my own for the very kind reception you have given us. It is an especial pleasure to the Duchess and myself to come here to-day, as my father laid the foundation stone of the new building in 1897, and therefore we are completing the work, so to speak, which he inaugurated." (Cheers.) " As Mr. Sturgis told us just now, of late years the number of patients increased so enormously that the old buildings were found quite in-adequate to their wants, and the Committee were compelled to seek a larger site for this new building. And, if I may be allowed to do so, I wish to congratulate the architects on the excellent result of their labours, and I also wish to congratulate the Committee and the medical staff on occu-pying a new Hospital designed and equipped according to the most modern requirements. The cost of maintenance of these new buildings, which cover three-quarters of an acre, will be, I fear, as Mr. Sturgis has just told us, very heavy, but I am sure the Committee deserve the generous support of the charitable public to enable them to continue the useful work that has been so ably carried out by this Hospital for nearly a century, and I can only say that I trust that the public will come forward and help this Hospital and prevent it from getting into debt by their annual subscriptions. I have now much pleasure in de-claring this new building open, and the Duchess joins with me in wishing the Royal London Ophthalmic Hospital continued prosperity in this new building, and a long career in its great and important work." (Cheers.)

Their Royal Highnesses then left the building, and were heartily cheered by a large crowd in the street as they drove away.

As a lasting memorial of the visit of their Royal High-nesses the Children's Ward was named the " Princess May " Ward. After their visit, they consented to become Patrons, and presented copies of their portraits to the Hospital, with their autographs attached.

The hopes expressed by Mr. Sturgis, the Chairman of the

Committee, at this opening ceremony, that increased financial support would be forthcoming to meet the additional
annual expenditure, were completely shattered for a time
by the outbreak of the South African War. As at the time
of the Crimean War, the sympathies and contributions
of the public became diverted to funds for soldiers and
sailors, and the donations and new subscriptions to the
Hospital almost ceased to come in, the result being that the
Hospital, in September, 1900, found itself £5,000 in debt.

One of the largest and most unforeseen items in increased
expenditure, resulting from the removal of the Hospital,
was the enormous addition to the amount in rates which it
was called upon to pay. The Hospital at Moorfields was
assessed by the City of London Union at a nominal amount,
the rates for the year 1897 being only £88. The Holborn
Union, in whose area the new building was situated, adopted
a different course, and the rates for 1900 amounted to £870,
nearly an eleventh part of the Hospital's annual total expenditure. In 1901 they increased to £948, and in 1902
to £972. No other hospital in London was assessed so
highly in proportion to its income and size, St. Thomas's and
Guy's being the only London hospitals paying heavier rates.

In answer to an appeal against such excessive rating the
authorities replied that, as the Hospital relieves patients
from every part of London, as well as many parts of the
country, they could not treat it on the footing of a local
charity.

In 1900 the Hospital, owing to its embarrassed financial
condition, was in arrears with the payment of two instal-
ments of rates, amounting to £324, and a summons was
served on it. The Justice of the Peace who had to deal
with the matter stated " that he had no other course but
to order payment within fourteen days." This summons
became widely reported and commented on in the public
press; considerable sympathy with the Hospital was thereby
evoked, and in the course of three days donations and sub-

scriptions came in, amounting to £300, which enabled it temporarily to meet its difficulties. Ever since, however, the annual amount which it has had to pay in rates has fluctuated between £800 and £1,000. Thus this Institution, which every year rescues numbers of people from loss of sight and from becoming rate-supported, has to raise this large sum in voluntary contributions from the benevolent public to pay out in rates.

Until the year 1875 hospitals were not regarded as ratable, as there was no obvious person connected with them to be assessed. In that year, however, the House of Lords ruled that voluntary hospitals had no right to such exemption and must pay rates as other premises, though no one's sense of justice had appeared to be offended. If, as they so frequently profess, public bodies wish to aid and support the work of voluntary hospitals, no more efficient method could be found than to exempt them again from this inconsistent and burdensome form of taxation. In connection with the Rating and Valuation Bill, which was before the House of Commons in July, 1928, a discussion on the rating of hospitals took place, being raised in connection with an amendment proposed by Mr. Harris, Member for South-West Bethnal Green, and seconded by Mr. Briant, Member for North Lambeth. The Minister of Health, Mr. Neville Chamberlain, whilst expressing his sympathy with the matter, did not consider the Bill to be one in which relief of that kind to hospitals could be given effect, it being for the stimulation of industries, and he refused to consider that the maintenance of the health of the community was likely to give such stimulation.

What at first seemed likely to be a most severe blow to the Hospital's means of maintenance ultimately resulted in its salvation. This was the establishment of the Prince of Wales' Hospital Fund (afterwards King Edward's Hospital Fund), and the diversion to it of annual subscriptions previously paid to the Hospital—*e.g.*, the Drapers' Company, which had for several years given a subscription of ten guineas, notified in 1900 that it would in future be discontinued as the Company was subscribing annually to the Prince of Wales' Fund. The receipt of the following letter was, therefore, a source of immense relief and satisfaction to all connected with the Hospital:

" THE PRINCE OF WALES' HOSPITAL FUND FOR LONDON.

" THE BANK OF ENGLAND,
" 27th December, 1901.

" THE TREASURER,
" ROYAL LONDON OPHTHALMIC HOSPITAL,
" CITY ROAD, E.C.

" SIR,

" By the desire of His Royal Highness, the President, I have the honour to enclose a cheque for £2,850.

" Of this sum, £900 is an annual grant to open eighteen closed beds, on the condition that by the opening of these beds eighteen more are made available for the sick poor in your Hospital; and the balance of £1,250 is a special donation for this year.

" I am also directed to inform you that your building is reported on as a very fine new building. The Visitors state that all the Wards, Operating Rooms, etc., are thoroughly practical and up-to-date, and that your very complete Hospital requires considerable additional funds to carry on its useful work.

" Kindly acknowledge the receipt of the above.

" Yours faithfully,
" (Signed) S. CROSSLEY,
" Honorary Secretary."

In June, 1902, His Majesty the King himself became an annual subscriber of ten guineas to the Hospital.

In December, 1902, a still more liberal grant was made by the King Edward's Hospital Fund for London, as shown by the following letter:

" SIR,

" I am directed by His Royal Highness the President to enclose a cheque for £4,500.

" Of this sum, £900 is an annual grant to support 18
beds opened by the aid of this Fund.   The balance, which
consists of £1,100 as an annual grant and £2,500 as a special
donation for this year, is given on the condition that 30
more beds are opened in your Hospital so that by opening
those beds 30 more are made available for the sick poor
in your Institution.

" Kindly acknowledge the receipt of the above.

" Yours faithfully,

" (Signed) SAVILE CROSSLEY,

" *Honorary Secretary.*"

The wards in the new Hospital were constructed to hold
138 beds, but at first, owing to its serious financial deficiency,
only 70 could be made available for use.   By the help of
the King's Hospital Fund in 1901, 18 more were opened
up, and, in the following year, by the help of the same fund,
an additional 30, leaving only 20 vacant.   The opening
of the wards containing the additional 30 beds in 1902
was made a ceremonial occasion by the visit to the Hospital
in state of the Lord Mayor and some of the Sheriffs of the
City of London.

In order to pay off its liabilities, the Committee of Management, during 1902, had to obtain a loan of £5,000 on the
security of the Harry Sedgwick Trust Fund, £7,000 of which
was retained by the Charity Commissioners until such time
as the compound interest on it had sufficiently accumulated
to repay the loan.   The annual income of the Hospital was
thereby temporarily reduced by the interest on these two
amounts.   In 1909, by the realisation of certain legacies,
the Hospital was enabled to repay this loan, the dividends
on the fund then reverting to it.

To find some fresh source of income it was agreed, at
a joint meeting of the Committee of Management and the
Medical Council, to try experimentally what could be
obtained by asking each out-patient on admission to make
a voluntary contribution, no compulsion to do so on any
account being used.   At the end of three months it was

found that an annual amount of £1,150 could be obtained in this way, without giving any offence to those solicited for help.

The way in which the new building was constructed necessitated some changes in the customs of the staff. The out-patient department was entirely separated from the in-patients, and it was thought desirable that the two classes of patients should be kept completely apart. This necessitated a second operating room specially for out-patients, for which provision had been made, and over which a special sister was appointed to preside. In the immaculate in-patient operating theatre it became the established custom for the surgeons working there to wear sterilised white cotton coats, instead of their ordinary ones, as they had done previously.

It may also be noted how customs have changed with regard to the hirsute appendages of the face in the members of the medical staff at different epochs. In the first half of the nineteenth century, all the members of the staff wore side whiskers. During the Crimean War our soldiers grew beards, and on their return beards became the fashion of the time. The surgeons at Moorfields, from the middle of the century up to the commencement of what may be described as the aseptic era, all wore beards. No surgeon on the staff now wears a beard; they are all either clean-shaven, or at most wear a closely-cut moustache.

The costume of the in-patients when taken into the operating theatre also needed consideration, and in the provision for them of special overalls the idea of a ladies' working guild first originated. The following description of its commencement and early progress was given in its Fifth Annual Report, dated December 31st, 1904:

" In the winter of the year 1900, Mrs. Quarry Silcock, Mrs. Treacher Collins, and the matron, Miss Richards, with a few other ladies who had special opportunities of knowing the difficulties with which the Hospital had to contend for lack of funds and public interest, banded themselves together and determined to help the Institution. They formed themselves into a Committee under the Presidency of Lady John Tweedy, and were fortunate in inducing many of their friends to join them. They determined to take upon themselves the essentially womanly task of supplying all the clothing, house and bed linen required in the Hospital for the use of the patients, and so successful were they that, not only were they able to do this, but by the end of the second year they were in a position to hand the sum of £50 to the general funds. The movement has since so far grown that many more necessaries have been added. The beds in the new wards, opened in 1903, were supplied with blankets, coverlets, and sheets from the fund, and the Guild has for the past two years maintained a Cot and a Woman's bed in the wards. It also extends its operations in other directions that can be of help to the Hospital. Through the consideration of several members, the Nurses' library has been replenished with interesting and useful books. Other members have rendered personal service by visiting at the Hospital, and have thus relieved the monotony of the hours spent by the suffering patients by reading pleasant books, entering into kindly conversation with them, and amusing them with singing and music. The cheering effect of such visits and the assistance they are in the work of recovery cannot be overestimated."

Extensive as were the improvements in the new Hospital over the old, in course of time fresh requirements cropped up, and it was discovered that some of the arrangements might have been better still. Any imperfections cannot, however, be attributed to oversight on the part of the architect, but rather to want of foresight and imagination on the part of those from whom he received instructions as to what to provide for. When first the rebuilding of the Hospital was decided on, the question was discussed as to whether the out-patient consulting room should be constructed to allow for accommodation of an increase in the number of the surgical staff, and the decision was deliberately arrived at that no such increase was desirable or likely to be required.

By the appointment of Soelberg Wells as an additional assistant-surgeon in 1867, the number of the surgical staff became increased to nine. Three surgeons attended each day and each came twice a week. Such an evenly balanced arrangement worked satisfactorily for a number of years. In 1867 the number of new out-patients was 17,211; in 1900 the number had increased to 36,932—i.e., more than double. The work entailed in dealing with this large increase of patients was, however, far more than double in amount to what it was in 1867, because sight-testing and the correction of errors of refraction had increased both in extent and accuracy. It is not surprising, therefore, that those surgeons who had but few clinical assistants found themselves unable to cope with all the demands made on them. In 1890 the post of paid refraction assistant had been created to aid the staff in that class of work. T. Phillips held this post for a number of years: he attended daily and became exceedingly expert in dealing with a large number of cases in a very short time. When, however, he was absent on a holiday or from illness, those who relied upon his assistance experienced great difficulties in getting through their work, patients even sometimes having to be sent away unseen.

In 1900 the Committee of Management determined that some fresh arrangement was essential, and advocated the appointment of additional assistant-surgeons: after considerable discussion this was agreed to, and the surgical staff was increased to twelve. The three new members to be appointed were to rank as assistant-surgeons, and their work was to be confined to the out-patients, except in the absence of the surgeon of the day. This was a reversion to a former plan, which after a short trial broke down, each member of the staff again attending to both out- and in-patients. Fortunately at that time there were a large number of able clinical assistants, who became candidates for the new posts, from amongst whom Percy Flemming, assistant ophthalmic surgeon at University College Hospital, J. Herbert Fisher, assistant ophthalmic surgeon at St. Thomas's Hospital, and Arnold Lawson (afterwards Sir Arnold, and ophthalmic surgeon at the Middlesex Hospital) were elected.

The result of this increase of the staff was that the out-patient consulting room, originally designed to accommodate three surgeons and their clinical assistants, had to accommodate four.

When the number of beds in use became increased to 118, the services of a third house surgeon were found requisite, those of the two senior being required for the in-patients, and those of the junior being confined to the out-patients. No accommodation had been made in the new building for an increase in the resident staff, and some reconstruction of rooms became necessary.

The accommodation required for the nursing staff had been sadly underestimated, and a part of the building which had been designed as an isolation quarters for sick nurses had to be taken into general use. At the present time, even with these additional rooms, it would be impossible to make use of all the beds for in-patients with which the Hospital is provided without first securing increased accommodation for nurses.

A nurse may have completed three years' training at a general hospital and have acquired sufficient theoretical knowledge to pass the examination which is considered essential before she is granted a certificate, and yet be incompetent to nurse a case of eye disease.

Moorfields Hospital has become, not only a special training school for ophthalmic surgeons, but also for ophthalmic nurses. Many who have been trained there have subsequently been appointed to take charge of ophthalmic institutions or departments in various parts of the United Kingdom, in the Colonies, and in America.

In 1896 courses of lectures given by members of the

surgical staff were instituted for nurses, in addition to the instruction which they received from the matron: such courses have been regularly carried on ever since.   In 1907 arrangements were made with the authorities of the Queen Victoria's Jubilee Institute for Nurses to allow of the district nurses employed by them to attend at the Hospital and receive practical instruction in ophthalmic nursing free of charge.   Fifty-three such nurses attended at the Hospital in 1907, and fresh ones have continued to attend ever since.

A large room was set apart in the new Hospital as a lecture theatre, and, as the teaching became more systematised and the number of students steadily increased, it became desirable to have a Dean appointed to advise the students as to their studies, and to superintend the classes: to this post W. T. Holmes Spicer was elected in 1899.   The teaching at Moorfields up to 1920, when the Royal Colleges of Physicians and Surgeons established a Diploma of Ophthalmology, had been post-graduate and almost entirely clinical and pathological, the laboratory and museum affording excellent facilities for the latter.   In order to obtain the Diploma of Ophthalmology it became necessary for students to pass a first examination in optics, and in the anatomy and physiology of the parts concerned in ophthalmic surgery. To meet the requirements of candidates for this examination, Moorfields then instituted special courses of instruction in these scientific subjects, upon which the practice of ophthalmology must always be based.   In so doing it has become a complete school of ophthalmology.

Graefe, in his work on the ocular muscles, described what are termed latent squints—*i.e.*, squints which only become manifest when the desire to see singly with the two eyes is removed.   Increased attention to them was awakened in 1886 when Stevens of New York suggested a convenient form of nomenclature to describe their different varieties, and in 1890 when Maddox of Bournemouth introduced a simple and expeditious method for their detection and measurement. Some enthusiasts at first tended to exaggerate the importance of these defects in the balance of the ocular muscles, attributing to them numerous ills to which the flesh is heir, and practising operative procedures for their correction. On the other hand, some were slow in devoting sufficient attention to them. Had more importance been attached to them at Moorfields, at the time the new building was under construction, better provision might have been made in it for their investigation.

In the closing years of the nineteenth century the science of bacteriology increased both in its importance and in its technique by leaps and bounds. In 1901 the medical staff, finding that more bacteriological investigations were required than the pathologist had time to devote to them in association with his other duties, recommended the establishment of a special bacteriological department and the appointment of a special bacteriologist. This entailed the provision of additional laboratory accommodation, and it was not until six years later that the Committee could see their way to the erection of a new laboratory above that part of the pathological department occupied by the Museum and curator's room, part of a legacy left to the Hospital by the late Mr. Samuel Lewis being used to defray the cost.

John Tweedy, who had been elected on the staff at the comparatively early age of twenty-nine, resigned in 1900 at the age of fifty-one, and was appointed consulting surgeon, the Committee of Management putting on record at the time its appreciation of the "numerous occasions he had "pleaded the cause of the Hospital in powerful and most interesting public addresses, endorsing his advocacy with liberal donations to its funds." Tweedy was a fluent and learned writer; he served for a long time on the editorial staff of the *Lancet*, so that most of his contributions appeared anonymously. He did not contribute much to the literature of ophthalmology, though he had had a very large

PLATE XXVI.

SIR JOHN TWEEDY, LL.D.

[To face p. 202

experience and was frequently called into consultation by his colleagues in difficult cases. An American student once asked him which he considered the best textbook on ophthal-mology. Tweedy took a deep breath, with which, on account of some chest affection, he always preceded any oratorical remark, and, with a dramatic wave of the arm towards a crowd of patients that were waiting to see him, said: " There, that is the best textbook."

Three years after his retirement from the staff of the Hospital, he became President of the Royal College of Surgeons; he held that post for three years, and was knighted in 1906. He possessed remarkable administrative capacity, and was skilful in putting through the business of a meeting with efficiency and dispatch. He also presided over the Ophthalmological and Medico-Legal Societies, the Medical Defence Union, and the Royal Medical Benevolent Fund. He died in 1924 at the age of seventy-five.

With the discovery of the ophthalmoscope the interests of ophthalmologists became largely medical as well as surgical; though they still style themselves ophthalmic surgeons, some might more aptly be termed ophthalmic physicians; Marcus Gunn was one of these. The distin-guished neurologist, Sir William Gowers, in 1879, wrote a book on *Medical Ophthalmoscopy*, which was the leading manual of its kind for many years; its third edition, which appeared in 1890, was edited by Marcus Gunn. He was a most careful ophthalmoscopic observer, and for several years devoted his attention to certain changes in the retinal bloodvessels. Writing on the outcome of these observations in 1898, he said:

" The chief importance of this retinal arterial change lies in its association with a more general arterial disease of a similar nature, particularly in the kidneys and brain, and in its prognostic value in regard to the results which may follow in cerebral vessels. It has been well said that ' a man is as old as his arteries.' I would urge that ophthalmoscopic observation is one of the most ready clinical means for the early detection of important arterial changes."

Rheumatism is a term which is applied to a multiple of ills, and during the nineteenth century a number of cases of inflammation of the iris were so classified. The most typical and well-defined form of rheumatism is rheumatic fever or acute articular rheumatism, and investigations of a number of such cases at general hospitals, and of cases of iritis at Moorfields, showed that the two affections were but rarely associated. Iritis not uncommonly occurs in connection with inflammation of the joints due to gonorrhœa, which is sometimes termed " gonorrhœal rheumatism," but a very large number of cases of iritis are met with unassociated with any joint affection or any venereal disease. Of recent years, largely as the outcome of the observations and teaching of William Lang, it has become recognised that such cases are secondary to some focus of inflammation elsewhere in the body, very often a septic condition in connection with the teeth. Seeing how many people suffer from septic teeth who never develop iritis, considerable scepticism at first prevailed as to its being the cause of the disease. The satisfactory way in which iritis subsides and ceases to recur after the septic focus in the mouth has been removed seems, however, to have definitely established the relation of the one to the other, and provided a means of eradicating a very potent cause of suffering and destruction of sight.

The reawakening of the importance of the medical side of ophthalmology made the surgical staff desirous in 1899 of securing for their patients at the Hospital the aid and assistance of a physician who had had a special training as a neurologist. For this purpose, it was decided to appoint a second physician who should be required to attend the Hospital once a week to examine and report on such cases as were selected for him by the surgical staff. Dr. James

PLATE XXVII.

WILLIAM LANG.

[To face p. 204

Taylor, who had studied under Dr. Hughlings Jackson, and who may be regarded as one of his most ardent disciples, was elected to this post.

The systematic and orderly keeping at Moorfields of the clinical records of in-patients, and of the pathological examination of the eyes removed, over a number of years by successive house surgeons and curators of the Museum, has provided a large amount of valuable material for the investigation of the natural history of certain diseases from which useful inferences as to their incidence and prognosis can be drawn. Such method of investigation has been applied by a succession of workers, over a period of fifty-seven years, to the different forms of malignant growths originating in the eyeball, and has added considerably to our knowledge concerning them, the results being published in the *Hospital Reports*.

A distinguished ophthalmic surgeon from New York who visited Moorfields went away much impressed by Nettleship, because he showed and discussed with him nothing but his failures. Most operating surgeons like to exhibit their successes and keep their disasters in the background, but by the study of our failures lies the road to future success. The curator of the Museum at Moorfields, or pathologist as he is now called, has the opportunity of examining critically all the eyes removed after the failure of operative procedures by the various members of the staff. From such examinations much valuable information has been collected and published, both in connection with operations for the removal of cataract and for the relief of glaucoma. To have had the advantage of carrying out these examinations must necessarily be an excellent training for one who is to become an operator himself. It is not, therefore, surprising that all those who have in recent years held the post of pathologist have subsequently been promoted to the surgical staff.

C. Devereux Marshall, who held the post of curator of

the Museum from 1894 to 1899, was elected assistant-surgeon on the retirement of Tweedy from the staff. William T. Lister (now Sir William Lister, K.C.M.G.) was the curator from 1899 to 1901, and was elected assistant-surgeon on the retirement of Waren Tay in 1904. John Herbert Parsons (now Sir John Parsons, C.B., F.R.S.) was curator from 1901 to 1905, and was elected assistant-surgeon to fill the vacancy caused by the death of A. Quarry Silcock in 1904.

When, in 1891, elementary education was made universal and compulsory, those responsible for the measure little realised all that it would involve. They little thought that in 1927 it would lead to the provision of 16,000,000 meals for school-children, and the medical examination of 2,000,000, involving the employment of about 2,000 doctors, 600 dentists, and 5,000 nurses, or that it would develop into what Sir George Newman, the chief medical officer of the Board of Education, describes as " the grand inquest of the nation directed towards laying the foundation of the nation's health."

It soon became evident that it was futile to compel children to study if their physical condition was such that they would not profit thereby, or if it was likely to lead to their physical deterioration. The question of their eyesight and its possible impairment from study early attracted attention. At first the teachers of the London School Board were given instructions to test the children's eyesight, and to give the parents of those in whom they found it defective a printed paper, stating that their child was suffering from a defect of vision, and, in the child's interests, they were strongly advised to consult an oculist without delay. To this notice was attached a list of hospitals with eye clinics and the times at which they were open for patients. The periodic rush of school-children with their parents to these clinics created chaos in their ordinary working routine.

In 1908 the Board of Education issued a circular stating that suitable provision can be made by a local education authority for the prescription and purchase of spectacles; and that, in this connection, the Board will be prepared to entertain proposals for contributions to the funds of hospitals on terms of adequate advantage, and the contributions are specially desirable in the case of eye hospitals. Also that " it is permissible to include among the conditions of contribution a provision allocating a reasonable remuneration to the medical men working for such institutions."

In the following year, in response to the invitation of the London County Council Education Committee, the Committee of the Hospital agreed to co-operate with it for the treatment of children whose eyes required attention, on the basis that not less than 3,000 nor more than 6,000 children be sent during the year, and that the Council would pay for the extra assistants which the Committee would have to appoint to carry out the work.

When the new Hospital was built, a portion of it on the ground floor had been left uncompleted, it being thought that it might ultimately be used as a chapel. The chaplain found it most convenient to conduct his services in the day wards. So, in 1909, through the generous help of some friends of the Hospital, donations were collected for the special purposes of carrying out certain alterations to this unoccupied part of the building to provide and equip a refraction department for school-children, separate from the other out-patients. This school-children's department was completed and became ready for use in 1910. While the majority of the children which attend require spectacles for the correction of errors of refraction, some are found to be suffering from some other affections of the eye, and these are referred for treatment to the ordinary out-patient department.

On the death of Queen Victoria, who had been a Patron throughout the whole of her long reign, in 1901, King

Edward VII. and Queen Alexandra consented to continue the patronage of the Institution which they had extended to it as Prince and Princess of Wales. In the same way, the Prince and Princess of Wales agreed to continue the patronage which they had bestowed on it when Duke and Duchess of York.

On the removal to the new Hospital, it had been foreseen that special steps would have to be taken to provide for the payment of the ground rent of £1,210 a year, and in 1899 John Tweedy started the " Rent Fund " with a generous donation of £150, to which he later added a further donation of £50. Owing, however, to the South African War and the pressing need to defray current expenses, but very slow progress was made in the collection of donations to this fund. In 1904, to celebrate the centenary of the foundation of the Hospital, the Committee decided to change the name of the fund to that of the " Centenary Fund," and to make a special appeal for contributions to it, all donations to be invested and the interest on it devoted to the payment of the rent.

A Centenary Festival Dinner was held at the Hotel Cecil on May 10th, over which Sir Charles Wyndham presided, delivering a most eloquent appeal on behalf of the Charity. The following ladies kindly acted as hostesses on the occasion: Princess Alexis Dolgorouki, the Hon. Helen Henniker, Lady Critchett, Lady Burnand, Lady Wyndham, Lady Walker, Mrs. Marcus Gunn, Mrs. Widenham Fosbery, Mrs. Edward Nettleship, Mrs. F. C. Scotter, Mrs. Beerbohm Tree, Mrs. Brooman-White of Arddaroch, Mrs. J. S. Wood. Three hundred guests were present, and the proceeds of the dinner, amounting to £2,270, were added to the Centenary Fund.

In former times it was the custom to end a story by drawing a moral; all such moral conclusions are nowadays regarded as out of fashion, and even a plot is no longer considered as essential in a story. All that is required is just to describe a slice out of life, beginning anywhere and ending when the requisite number of pages have been filled. This story of the Moorfields Eye Hospital describes a slice out of the life of an institution, commencing with its foundation in 1804, and ending, whilst it is still full of progressive vigour, with the celebration of its centenary.

Most people will agree that the chief object of raking over the ashes of the past should be to acquire inspirations for the future; and so, though it may be hopelessly out of fashion, this story will conclude with some maxims which may be deduced from all that has gone before.

The general principle on which the Hospital was established was that the treatment of diseases of the eye and visual disorders should be recognised as a branch of medicine and surgery, and not left in the hands of unqualified and imperfectly trained practitioners. With this end in view, it has always been insisted on that the members of its medical staff should hold the highest possible qualifications as physicians and surgeons, and that every encouragement should be given to qualified medical men to come to it to study the treatment of eye diseases as a branch of medicine and surgery. The necessity for the recognition of this general principle, now in 1929, is just as necessary as in 1804, there being, as then, no short road to the efficient treatment of visual defects apart from a complete training as a medical practitioner.

The question is sometimes asked: Do special hospitals justify their existence ? The perusal of this book, it is hoped, will at any rate show that the Moorfields Eye Hospital has justified its existence.

One of the incomparable advantages afforded by a special hospital is the field which it offers for mass observation, both clinical and pathological. It was by taking advantage of the extensive opportunities for clinical research which Moorfields Hospital affords that Sir William Lawrence, Sir Jonathan Hutchinson, Dr. Hughlings Jackson, Edward

Nettleship, and others have been able to make their most valuable contributions to our knowledge of the natural history of eye diseases.

Pathological research in connection with eye disease depends almost entirely on the investigation of eyes which have had to be removed during life, and at Moorfields the custom of placing the mass of such material at the disposal of one man, the curator of the Museum, whilst he holds office, has proved to be of inestimable advantage in the promotion of that line of research.

To arrive at an accurate estimate of the benefits to be derived from any special line of treatment or from some operative procedure, it is necessary that it should be tried in the various varieties and phases of a disease; inferences drawn from isolated cases must always prove fallible. The mass of cases provided by a special hospital allows of reliable estimates being arrived at.

The facilities for mass observation which a special hospital affords are of as great advantage to the student as to the investigator. It enables him, not only to get a comprehensive picture of a disease in all its manifestations firmly impressed on his mind, but also to see in a comparatively short time several examples of what, in a more restricted sphere, would be regarded as rare affections. It has been the recognition of such advantages that has induced medical men from all parts of the world, for over a hundred years, to congregate at Moorfields to gain instruction and experience.

It has not, however, been only the size of the clinic which has attracted students of ophthalmology to Moorfields, but also to a large extent the personnel of its medical staff. To listen to discussions on debatable matters by able exponents, holding forth day after day from the same pulpits, and to watch varying forms of procedure on similar conditions carried out in the same theatre by different operators, stimulates students to observe and to think for themselves

—a form of training which is far preferable to the absorption of dogmatic aphorisms from a single teacher, or the attendance at courses of didactic oratory.

Medicine and surgery are not exact sciences, and probably never will be; any increase in exactitude in connection with them may, however, be regarded as synonymous with progress. The immense increase in exactitude in connection with ophthalmology which has taken place since the discovery of the ophthalmoscope can be realised, if we consider the number of well understood conditions which are now differentiated, and which were formerly grouped under the vague heading of " Amaurosis." Ophthalmology is closely associated with such exact sciences as mathematics, chemistry, and physics. It was, indeed, from the association of the latter with ophthalmology that the discovery of the ophthalmoscope resulted; for, as Helmholtz himself said, " When a well-trained physicist came and grasped the importance of such an instrument, nothing more was wanted, since all the knowledge had been developed which was required for its construction."

William Cumming had grasped the possibilities of such a discovery, but, lacking himself the necessary training in physics and failing to consult anyone who had, missed the way to the end for which he was striving.

It was the fortunate circumstance of Sir James Mackenzie Davidson being interested in both physics and ophthalmology, at the time of Professor Röntgen's discovery of the X-rays in 1895, that led to their early employment at Moorfields in connection with foreign bodies implanted in the eyeball, and the introduction of an accurate method for their localisation.

Of the intimate association of mathematics with ophthalmology we have evidence in Helmholtz's great work on physiological dioptrics. Donders, in the preface to his book *On the Anomalies of Accommodation and Refraction of the Eye, with a Preliminary Essay on Physiological Dioptrics,* published by the New Sydenham Society in 1844, writes as follows:

" In the doctrine of the anomalies of refraction and accommodation, the connection between science and practice is more closely drawn together than in any part of medicine.

" Science here celebrates her triumph, for it is at her hand that this branch has acquired the exact character which makes it also worthy of the attention of natural philosophers and physiologists. It is, indeed, satisfactory to see, how in the accurate distinction between anomalies of refraction and accommodation with exclusion of every condition foreign to those anomalies, the system assumed, as if spontaneously, an elegant simplicity; and how the cause and mode of origin of many an obscure type of disease emerged into the clearest light.

" Practice, in connection with science, here enjoys the rare but splendid satisfaction of not only being able to give infallible precepts based upon fixed rules, but also of being guided by a clear insight into the principles of her actions—advantages the more highly to be estimated as the anomalies in question are of more frequent occurrence, and as they more deeply affect the use and functions of the eyes.

" Is it, then, strange that the study and treatment of my subject have been to me a labour of love ? the more so, as I felt proud in having been called upon to elaborate it for a country in which Young, Wells, Ware, Brewster, and Airy have pointed out to us the track which we had only to follow, and happy in being able to offer my work in this form to my highly esteemed friends and colleagues, whose proofs of kindness and affection have left with me the most agreeable recollections of my visits to England."

In its indebtedness to chemistry, ophthalmology shares with all other branches of medicine and surgery. It was to the chemist Louis Pasteur that we owe the upgrowth of the new science of bacteriology. It is to Madame Curie's chemical researches that we are indebted for radium, which promises to be the most effectual means for dealing with malignant neoplasms apart from operations.

It is to Wassermann that we owe the possibility of a

chemical means of diagnosing syphilis, and to Ehrlich a chemical compound which will kill the invading organism without damaging the tissue of the infected host.

From what has gone before it would seem that measures, which tend to bring about a close association between the clinical work in the Hospital and the laboratory work of the trained observers in these exact sciences, are those most likely to prove fruitful in the promotion of the progress of ophthalmology in the future.

Hospitals in the first part of the nineteenth century were institutions founded and supported by the rich for the relief of suffering in the indigent poor, the inmates admitted to which were given everything for nothing.

Under altered conditions, they are now rapidly becoming institutions for the relief of suffering in the community at large, supported in part by donations from munificent persons, and in part by contributions from those who receive benefits in them.

In former times the word " hospital " raised in the mind a picture of a barrack-like building, associated with pain and suffering, with poverty and death.

John Couper, when senior surgeon at the London Hospital, was journeying to it down the Mile End Road in one of the old horse-drawn omnibuses, and asked the conductor to put him down at the London Hospital; the conductor shouted out to the driver, " Stop at the slaughter-house, Bill."

Since the introduction of anæsthetics and antiseptics hospitals are no longer regarded as slaughter-houses by the general public, but as places where pain and suffering are relieved, and health and vigour are restored. No longer are they forbidding barrack-like structures, but temples of hygienic cleanliness. No longer is it a luxury to be ill, or to have an operation performed in one's own home, where all the necessary appliances have to be imported or improvised. Far preferable has it become to go to an institution specially constructed for such purposes, furnished with the most up-to-date contrivances, and with a staff efficiently trained to meet all emergencies.

In a Report of a Special Committee of the King Edward's Hospital Fund for London on " Pay Beds," dated July, 1928, the present relation of various sections of the general public to hospitals is set out as follows:

" During recent years there has been a considerable extension, both of the classes included amongst Voluntary Hospital patients and of the payments made by ordinary patients. There was a time when the Hospitals were only called upon to provide comparatively simple treatments for the necessitous poor, which meant those who were unable to pay for medical attendance. With the development of expensive methods of treatment and diagnoses, large numbers of the middle and professional classes are now unable to pay the full cost of these services, some of which, according to our evidence, are often difficult to obtain outside the Hospital.

" At the same time, experience has shown that large numbers of the ordinary Hospital patients are both able and willing to contribute towards their cost. At present, therefore, there is a demand for Hospital treatment from several different classes which may be grouped into three: First, those who cannot afford to pay anything, and who receive, when in the ordinary wards, free maintenance and treatment; second, those who can and do contribute according to their means towards their cost of maintenance in the ordinary wards, though still receiving free medical attendance from the visiting staff of physicians and surgeons; third, those whose standard of living causes them to desire better accommodation, or at all events more privacy, than is provided in the ordinary wards, and who are prepared to pay for it according to their means, and also to pay something for medical attendance. Beyond these, there is a fourth class, those who can afford to obtain their treatment in private nursing homes and to pay full medical fees."

Institutions, like individuals, if they wish to survive in the struggle for existence, have to obey the universal law of adaptation to environment. Moorfields Hospital, during the first hundred years of its existence, has undergone reconstruction, had additions made to it, and has twice been removed to a new site, in response to the demands made upon it by the increasing number of patients attending for relief, and to the developments and discoveries in the methods of applying relief.

To be capable of such frequent fresh adaptations, an institution must be prepared to obey another biological law—that of retaining a high degree of plasticity, which, in the case of an institution, is equivalent to maintaining a big margin for expansion.

As has been shown, Moorfields is largely indebted to the foresight of its architects for having retained such a margin for expansion to meet new requirements. When first a new Hospital was erected on the Moorfields site, Sir Robert Smirke, the architect, advised the Committee to secure the freehold of a piece of vacant ground immediately behind the Hospital, upon which, after the discovery of the ophthalmoscope, a new out-patient department with a large darkroom was built. It was also, probably by his advice, that Dr. Farre secured the lease of the piece of ground on its south side, part of which he for a time let off for a stables and in part used for the Saunderian Institute, but upon which a new wing of the Hospital was subsequently built, when the demand for more in-patient accommodation became urgent, after the introduction of anæsthetics and the great increase in the number of operative procedures. When the removal to a new site again became necessary, it was the proceeds derived from the greatly enhanced value of these sites, which had been so fortunately obtained, that supplied the funds for the erection of the new building.

It was due to the advice of the architects, Keith Young and Bedell, that the large site in the City Road was chosen for the present Hospital, instead of the cramped one in Eldon Street adjoining the former building, to which at the time sentiment made a strong appeal.

In the twenty-five years which have elapsed since the celebration of the Hospital's centenary, fresh discoveries and altered economic conditions have produced further changes in environment, calling for more expansion in one direction and another. Fortunately, the plasticity of the present large site is by no means exhausted, and with suitable adaptation it is capable of providing all the demands likely to be made upon it for several years to come.

The last maxim, however, to be drawn from the past history of the Hospital is the necessity of keeping ever alert for adaptations to meet fresh changes in its environment as they arise.

APPENDIX

Presidents

	Date of Appointment.	Date of Resignation.
Sir Charles Price, Bart.	1804	1818
Mr. William Mellish	1818	1838
Rt. Hon. Earl Fitzwilliam ..	1838	1856
Mr. William Cotton, D.C.L., F.R.S.	1857	1867
Sir John Lubbock, F.R.S., M.P. (afterwards Lord Avebury) ..	1867	1913
His Royal Highness Prince Arthur of Connaught, K.G.	1914	

Chairmen of the Committee of Management

Mr. Harry Sedgwick	1804	1818
Mr. Ralph Price	1818	1830
Mr. Stuart Donaldson	1831	1837
Rev. J. Russell, D.D.	1837	1857
Mr. Richard Heathfield	1857	1859
Mr. F. G. Sambrooke	1860	1871
Mr. Philip Cazenove	1871	1879
Mr. Charles Gordon	1879	1897
Mr. H. P. Sturgis	1897	1921
Mr. Theodore W. Luling ..	1921	

Honorary Medical and Surgical Officers

Physicians

John Richard Farre, M.D. ..	1805	1857
Frederick J. Farre, M.D. ..	1843	1880
Robert Martin, M.D.	1856	1884
Sir Stephen Mackenzie, M.D. ..	1884	1905

	Date of Appointment.	Date of Resignation.
James Taylor, C.B.E., M.D. ..	1899	1919
Gordon M. Holmes, C.M.G., C.B.E., M.D.	1914	1927
William J. Adie, M.D.	1927	

Surgeons

J. Cunningham Saunders (Founder)	1804	Died 1810
Benjamin Travers, F.R.S. ..	1810	1817
Sir William Lawrence, Bart., F.R.S.	1814	1826
Frederick Tyrrell	1817	Died 1843
John Scott	1826	1846
Gilbert Mackmurdo, F.R.S. ..	1830	1856
John Dalrymple, F.R.S.	1832	1849
James Dixon	1843	1868
George Critchett	1843	1877
Sir William Bowman, Bart., F.R.S.	1846	1876
Alfred Poland	1848	1861
H. H. Mackmurdo	1851	1852
John C. Wordsworth	1852	1883
J. F. Streatfield	1856	Died 1886
J. W. Hulke, F.R.S.	1858	1890
George Lawson	1862	1891
Sir Jonathan Hutchinson, F.R.S.	1862	1878
John Couper	1866	1895
J. Soelberg Wells	1867	Died 1880
Waren Tay	1877	1904
James E. Adams	1877	1884
Sir John Tweedy, LL.D. ..	1878	1900
Robert Lyall	1880	Died 1882
Edward Nettleship, F.R.S. ..	1882	1898
R. Marcus Gunn	1883	1909
W. Lang	1884	1912
A. Quarry Silcock	1886	Died 1904
J. B. Lawford, LL.D.	1890	1918
A. Stanford Morton	1891	1909
E. Treacher Collins	1895	1922
W. T. Holmes Spicer	1898	1920
Percy Fleming	1900	1919
J. Herbert Fisher	1900	1927

	Date of Appointment.	Date of Resignation.
Sir Arnold Lawson, K.B.E.	1900	1914
C. Devereux Marshall	1900	Died on active service, 1918
Sir William T. Lister, K.C.M.G.	1904 1919	1905
Sir John Herbert Parsons, C.B.E., F.R.S.	1905	
Claud Worth	1905	1921
W. Ilbert Hancock	1909	Died 1910
George Coats	1909	Died 1915
Malcolm L. Hepburn	1910	1926
A. Cyril Hudson	1913	1928
R. Foster Moore, O.B.E.	1914	
R. Affleck Greeves	1915	
F. A. Juler	1918	
Charles Goulden, O.B.E.	1919	
B. T. Lang	1920	Died 1928
M. H. Whiting, O.B.E.	1921	
P. G. Doyne	1922	
Humphrey Neame	1926	
Miss Ida C. Mann	1927	
W. Stewart Duke-Elder	1928	
Rupert S. Scott	1928	

Ear, Nose, and Throat Surgeon

G. Seccombe Hett	1923	1929

Medical Officer to the X-Ray Department

Sir James Mackenzie Davidson	1899	1910
Albert Bowie	1910	

Dental Surgeons

Arthur E. Relph	1913	1915
R. M. Fickling	1915	1928
Stanley A. Riddett	1928	

Medical Officer to the Ultra-Violet Ray Department

W. Stewart Duke-Elder	1927

Secretaries

	Date of Appointment.	Date of Resignation.
Mr. Richard Battley	1804	1818
Mr. Matthew Heathfield	1818	1834
Mr. William Bircham	1835	1844
Mr. Robert Francis Dalrymple	1844	1846
Mr. F. A. Curling	1846	1856
Mr. Charles Gordelier	1856	1860
Mr. J. Mogford	1860	1872
Mr. Robert J. Newstead	1872	1897
Mr. Robert J. Bland	1897	1923
Mr. Arthur J. M. Tarrant	1924	

INDEX